Year 4 Maths Workbook

Addition and Subtraction, Times Tables, Fractions, Measurement, ... elling the Time and Statistics for 8-9 Year Olds | Homeschooling Reso... KS2 | YR4 | Y4

JUNGLE PUBLISHING

Introduction: How to use this book

This is a maths book for 8 - 9 year olds based on the National Curriculum in England (Year 4). It also can be used by those in Upper Key Stage 2 (Year 5 and Year 6) wanting to cement their knowledge.

The book is divided up into seven parts: Number and Place Value; Addition and Subtraction; Multiplication and Division; Fractions; Measurement; Geometry and Statistics as per the curriculum for Y4/ KS2.

Where you see the ⏱ symbol, this indicates a time trial and you should aim to complete the page you are on as quicky as possible. A guideline time will be given in seconds underneath the clock. Whilst the time trials should add fun it is important to remember that quality and understanding still remain the most important factors.

A marking/ scoring system is provided on each page to help measure progress. In addition to this, please use the progress chart on page 4 and 5 to help reflect on what parts of the book came more or less naturally.

Answers are included at the back.

Good luck!

This book belongs to:
....

Table of Contents

Progress Chart

Shade in the star when you've completed a section. For each section, jot down the questions that you found easy and those you found more difficult.

Section 1 - Number and Place Value

Completed ?	What did I find easy?	What did I find difficult?
☆		

Section 2 - Addition and Subtraction

Completed ?	What did I find easy?	What did I find difficult?
☆		

Section 3 - Multiplication

Completed ?	What did I find easy?	What did I find difficult?
☆		

Section 4 - Fractions

Completed ?	What did I find easy?	What did I find difficult?
☆		

Section 5 - Measurement

Completed ?	What did I find easy?	What did I find difficult?
☆		

Section 6 - Geometry

Completed ?	What did I find easy?	What did I find difficult?
☆		

Section 7 - Statistics

Completed ?	What did I find easy?	What did I find difficult?
☆		

Put the four numbers on the correct places on each line.

1) 70, 140, 10, 170

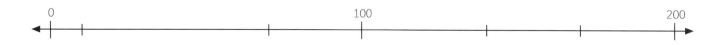

2) -960, -860, -930, -890

This time try without the guides.

3) 756, 726, 796, 906

Fill in the missing bricks to complete the patterns.

☐ (3)

1) | -15 | | -51 | | -87 |

2) | -75 | | | | -35 |

3) | -83 | | | | -107 | ☐

(3)

Score:

1

Counting Up and Down

Fill in the missing numbers. Hint: There is a pattern to each line of boxes.

1)

	600			582			564	558	

2)

	-6	-5			-2	-1			

3)

	196	203	210						252

4)

	297		279					234	225

☐ (4)

Fill in the table from left to right, row by row. Count by 9 from 40 to 391.

1)

40	49								
130						184			
220	229	238				274	283	292	301
310									391

☐ (30)

Score:

2

Determine the place value of the underlined digit. For example: '3 ones', or '6 tens'. The first one has been done for you.

1) 6,343 = _4 tens_

2) 418 = _____

3) 410 = _____

4) 5,375 = _____

5) 6,397 = _____

6) 4,724 = _____

7) 8,481 = _____

8) 4,032 = _____

9) 8,073 = _____

10) 4,721 = _____

Use partitioning to complete these sums, the first one is done for you. ☐

(9)

1) 7,567 = | 7,000 | + | 500 | + | 60 | + | 7 |

2) 8,764 = | ___ | + | ___ | + | ___ | + | ___ |

3) 4,567 = | ___ | + | ___ | + | ___ | + | ___ | ☐

(2)

Score:

Ordering Numbers

Order these numbers from smallest to largest.

The first one has been done for you.

1) 4,773 _253_   2) 2,865 _____   3) 3,780 _____
    890 _403_   1,271 _____   1,432 _____
    253 _816_   633   _____   733   _____
    816 _890_   2,675 _____   9,962 _____
    403 _4,773_   1,603 _____   410   _____

4) 2,314 _____   5) 6,186 _____   6) 999   _____
    6,783 _____   519   _____   5,995 _____
    2,838 _____   363   _____   411   _____
    864   _____   788   _____   4,015 _____
    854   _____   391   _____   7,727 _____ ☐

(5)

This time try from largest to smallest.

1) 301   _____   2) 952   _____   3) 2,851 _____
    8,025 _____   9,439 _____   7,689 _____
    7,633 _____   438   _____   711   _____
    9,208 _____   445   _____   1,807 _____
    320   _____   7,988 _____   5,726 _____ ☐

(3)

Score:

Circle the Numbers

60s

Look at the groups below and follow the instructions for each set.

Circle the smallest number

1)	2)	3)	4)
2,481	4,925	1,999	1,818
161	2,812	3,168	1,490
503	4,893	3,054	4,492
4,967	855	874	2,639
3,379	2,364	4,535	3,611

5)	6)	7)	8)
2,881	1,728	4,528	42
1,834	3,177	3,790	2,184
229	193	1,520	3,232
2,508	2,907	2,240	3,983
2,995	4,619	2,728	4,317

(8)

Circle the largest number

1)	2)	3)	4)
4,204	4,867	1,721	646
4,144	2,959	1,429	4,933
1,505	4,666	1,133	2,995
1,289	1,363	2,495	1,972
3,729	3,674	3,051	1,651

5)	6)	7)	8)
1,747	3,209	4,634	3,737
2,619	1,647	3,258	329
1,986	813	509	3,941
1,237	3,146	3,322	3,779
2,837	4,492	4,407	3,129

(8)

Time: :

Score:

5

Circle the Numbers 2

Circle the smallest and largest number in each group.

120s

1)	2)	3)	4)
2,404	426	1,821	3,772
401	728	3,483	1,426
874	1,528	4,615	83
1,386	3,738	1,104	88
474	2,147	4,437	1,548

5)	6)	7)	8)
4,168	4,567	3,027	735
4,238	3,194	2,633	3,253
1,840	1,394	3,798	2,343
2,340	3,816	2,588	901
3,049	3,669	1,470	1,812

(8)

Do the same again but, be wary, these sets include negative numbers too.

1)	2)	3)	4)
1,306	-707	-9,669	-5,246
536	-2,032	2,568	-3,526
1,488	2,078	-6,219	-9,197
2,699	2,569	-3,004	357
-1,308	-3,757	-2,292	-8,443

5)	6)	7)	8)
-344	391	-9,048	-294
-3,564	-7,238	-7,026	1,369
-5,443	-1,567	2,649	-1,740
-4,385	-737	1,530	19
2,119	2,940	-1,353	4,219

(8)

Time: :

Score:

Write these numbers as words.

1) 110,662 _____

2) 524,332 _____

3) 324,849 _____

4) 213,070 _____

5) 876,234 _____

(5)

Write these words as numbers.

1) _____ eight thousand nine hundred and eight

2) _____ thirty-nine thousand nine hundred and fifty-seven

3) _____ sixty-three thousand five hundred and forty-four

4) _____ fifteen thousand and sixty-eight

5) _____ fifty-six thousand four hundred and fifty-three

(5)

Score:

Before and After

Add the numbers which come either before, after or between those provided.

1) -1,306   -1,305 _____

2) _____ -2,585 _____

3) _____ -1,711 _____

4) _____ -9,465 _____

5) _____ -8,531 _____

6) -3,329 _____ -3,327

7) _____ -1,977 _____

8) -5,337 _____ -5,335

9) -4,208 _____

10) -2,052 _____

(9)

Round to the underlined digit. The first one is done for you.

1) 3,8<u>4</u>2 = _3 8 4 0_

2) 1,<u>1</u>10 = _____

3) <u>1</u>,879 = _____

4) 6,86<u>8</u> = _____

5) 9,<u>8</u>37 = _____

6) 3,92<u>2</u> = _____

7) 4,5<u>8</u>7 = _____

8) <u>4</u>,523 = _____

9) 1,3<u>4</u>8 = _____

10) 8,9<u>8</u>0 = _____

11) 4,<u>9</u>18 = _____

12) 9,72<u>0</u> = _____

(12)

Score:

The Romans used the following letters for numbers.

I	V	X	L	C	D	M
1	5	10	50	100	500	1000

Letters are combined to make numbers, written in order from largest to smallest.

Examples: 7 = VII; 15 = XV; 321 = CCCXXI

However, when more than three identical symbols are required, the number is written as a subtraction instead. Numbers involving 4, 9, 40, 90, 400 and 900 are written as subtractions with the subtracted number written before the larger number.

Examples: 9 = IX (10 -1) ; 42 XLII (50-10) +2 ; 90 = XC (100-10) ; 99 XCIX = (100-10) + (10 – 1);

400 = CD (500-100) ; 452 = CDLII (500-100) + (50 + 2) ; 900 = CM (1000-100)

Convert the values from numbers to Roman Numerals.

1) 19 =_____

2) 5 =_____

3) 100 = _____

4) 77 = _____

5) 82 = _____

6) 6 = _____

7) 80 = _____

8) 1 = _____

9) 53 = _____

10) 24 = _____

11) 51 = _____

12) 22 = _____

13) 49 = _____

14) 16 = _____

15) 31 = _____

Score :

Convert the values from Roman Numerals to numbers.

1) XCIII = _____

2) LXX = _____

3) IV = _____

4) VIII = _____

5) X = _____

6) VII = _____

7) VI = _____

8) I = _____

9) XXI = _____

10) XXIV = _____

11) V = _____

12) LI = _____

13) LIV = _____

14) LXXIV = _____

15) LXXXVIII = _____

Write the answer to these calculations in....

 (15)

a) Roman Numerals

b) Numbers

1) [XII] + [X] =

2) [IV] + [V] =

3) [C] + [VI] =

4) [M] + [C] =

 1) [XII] - [III] =

2) [CL] - [XXX] =

(6)

Score:

Work out the relationship between the inputs and outputs and fill in the blanks.
The first one has been done, with the relationship demonstrated underneath.

1)

Input	Output
107	153
39	85
41	87
172	218

Add 46

2)

Input	Output
141	190
4	53
89	
101	

3)

Input	Output
172	215
200	243
176	
94	

4)

Input	Output
57	137
79	159
126	
152	

5)

Input	Output
117	213
43	139
19	
14	

6)

Input	Output
61	97
165	201
170	
11	

☐

(5)

Shade the circle with the correct answer.

1)

89
+
621
=

(710) (851) (705)

(701) (716)

2)

75
-
127
=

(-44) (-53) (-52)

(-48) (-51)

☐

(2)

Score:

11

Table Drills

Complete the tables.

1)

+	22	14	52	26	97
834				860	
657					754
340					
225					
588					

2)

+	775	550	500	325	19
22					
15					
39				364	
500					
30			530		

Shade the correct sum.

☐
(2)

1) a)

22.2

+

101

=

130.3

b)

22.2

+

102

=

120.3

c)

21.2

+

102

=

123.2

d)

21.2

+

101

=

123.3

e)

22.2

+

102

=

123.3

☐
(1)

Score:

What can you add to the top number to make the bottom number?

90s

1)
51
+
70

2)
44
+
99

3)
58
+
69

4)
22
+
27

5)
108
+
138

6)
56
+
161

7)
101
+
197

8)
46
+
53

9)
83
+
187

10)
23
+
24

11)
76
+
151

12)
50
+
79

13)
79
+
183

14)
72
+
80

15)
140
+
174

16)
97
+
199

17)
59
+
111

18)
46
+
51

19)
33
+
90

20)
20
+
10

21)
45
+
102

22)
20
+
151

23)
169
+
180

24)
98
+
105

25)
99
+
111

Time: :

Score:

13

Number Bonds 2

90s

1) ____ + 98 = 119

2) 16 + ____ = 72

3) ____ + 52 = 115

4) ____ + 59 = 140

5) 80 + ____ = 154

6) ____ + 88 = 173

7) ____ + 44 = 75

8) 70 + 41 = ____

9) 62 + 99 = ____

10) ____ + 84 = 125

11) 83 + 99 = ____

12) 33 + 86 = ____

13) 67 + 67 = ____

14) 64 + ____ = 139

15) 54 + ____ = 67

16) 91 + 76 = ____

17) 98 + ____ = 181

18) 46 + 96 = ____

19) ____ + 16 = 97

20) ____ + 67 = 114

21) 40 + 38 = ____

22) 14 + 21 = ____

23) 92 + ____ = 121

24) 40 + ____ = 107

25) ____ + 20 = 56

26) 74 + ____ = 169

27) 45 + 95 = ____

28) ____ + 21 = 87

29) 74 + 28 = ____

30) 87 + ____ = 181

Time: :

Score:

1) 35
  + 127

2) 148
  + 46

3) 119
  + 37

4) 43
  + 47

5) 24
  + 94

6) 38
  + 34

7) 174
  + 16

8) 84
  + 17

9) 31
  + 160

10) 18
  + 107

11) 43
  + 48

12) 93
  + 73

13) 37
  + 95

14) 142
  + 48

15) 71
  + 30

16) 61
  + 10

17) 27
  + 55

18) 12
  + 151

19) 88
  + 103

20) 55
  + 70

21) 127
  + 42

22) 75
  + 87

23) 17
  + 89

24) 111
  + 45

25) 48
  + 107

26) 19
  + 172

27) 49
  + 116

28) 56
  + 73

29) 68
  + 56

30) 48
  + 85

Score:

Addition 0-500

1) 211
  + 224

2) 254
  + 150

3) 242
  + 227

4) 127
  + 202

5) 213
  + 198

6) 277
  + 190

7) 225
  + 228

8) 148
  + 127

9) 111
  + 120

10) 286
  + 186

11) 255
  + 234

12) 128
  + 287

13) 282
  + 172

14) 310
  + 111

15) 229
  + 140

16) 114
  + 156

17) 333
  + 123

18) 229
  + 196

19) 290
  + 103

20) 163
  + 288

21) 192
  + 135

22) 121
  + 197

23) 126
  + 354

24) 351
  + 107

25) 330
  + 161

26) 110
  + 116

27) 144
  + 289

28) 165
  + 283

29) 151
  + 349

30) 112
  + 103

Score:

1) 269
+ 379

2) 399
+ 174

3) 498
+ 188

4) 306
+ 359

5) 281
+ 452

6) 433
+ 104

7) 217
+ 172

8) 192
+ 227

9) 343
+ 364

10) 345
+ 404

11) 318
+ 361

12) 337
+ 121

13) 415
+ 343

14) 473
+ 268

15) 463
+ 348

16) 199
+ 393

17) 350
+ 380

18) 288
+ 444

19) 141
+ 425

20) 397
+ 462

21) 226
+ 279

22) 346
+ 169

23) 427
+ 328

24) 175
+ 253

25) 387
+ 190

26) 399
+ 353

27) 489
+ 450

28) 326
+ 408

29) 142
+ 378

30) 258
+ 254

Score:

Addition 0-10000

Add these 4 digit numbers.

1)   3,300
     + 3,344

2)   2,167
     + 4,832

3)   2,520
     + 2,593

4)   4,210
     + 1,147

5)   3,424
     +   254

6)   1,370
     + 1,818

7)   2,352
     + 3,476

8)   3,216
     + 2,582

9)   1,851
     + 1,746

10)   4,815
     + 4,651

11)   4,323
     +   502

12)   3,387
     + 4,736

13)   1,709
     +   399

14)   1,661
     + 1,219

15)   1,562
     + 4,033

16)   4,807
     + 4,026

17)   1,928
     + 3,080

18)   2,797
     + 1,313

19)   2,880
     + 3,276

20)   2,747
     + 4,370

Score:

Add these sets of three numbers together in your head.

1)
```
    35
    45
 +   9
_____
```

2)
```
     2
    26
 +  22
_____
```

3)
```
    13
    17
 +  41
_____
```

4)
```
    21
     2
 +   7
_____
```

5)
```
    30
    31
 +  38
_____
```

6)
```
    24
    49
 +   4
_____
```

7)
```
    33
    23
 +  38
_____
```

8)
```
    31
     4
 +  41
_____
```

9)
```
    40
     7
 +  49
_____
```

10)
```
    12
    47
 +  13
_____
```

11)
```
    17
    16
 +  46
_____
```

12)
```
    10
    37
 +  16
_____
```

13)
```
    39
    15
 +  11
_____
```

14)
```
    49
    38
 +  12
_____
```

15)
```
    28
    36
 +  29
_____
```

16)
```
    17
    28
 +  23
_____
```

17)
```
    25
    11
 +  23
_____
```

18)
```
    47
    38
 +  33
_____
```

19)
```
    26
     5
 +  42
_____
```

20)
```
    18
    12
 +  20
_____
```

Score:

Word Questions

Solve these addition word problems.

1) Sharon and Paul are baking cupcakes for a summer cake sale. Sharon bakes 160 cakes and Paul bakes 150 cakes. How many did they bake in total?

2) A theatre sells 168 tickets on Saturday and 184 tickets on Sunday. How many did they sell on that weekend?

3) Brian has gone travelling. One day he drives 177 miles and the next day he drives 155 miles. How many miles has he travelled altogether?

4) Janet has started a business. In the first week she sells £161 of goods; the second week she sells £191. What is the overall sales in pounds?

5) Audrey scores 178 at bowling and Adam scores 193, what is their combined score?

6) Allan and Marin play hockey together each weekend. Across the course of their careers, Allan has scored 178 goals and Marin has scored 196. What is their combined career tally?

Score:

90s

Subtract the following in your head.

1) 128
  − 100
  _____

2) 120
  − 90
  _____

3) 183
  − 152
  _____

4) 169
  − 71
  _____

5) 177
  − 34
  _____

6) 198
  − 58
  _____

7) 138
  − 88
  _____

8) 183
  − 127
  _____

9) 180
  − 161
  _____

10) 188
  − 179
  _____

11) 142
  − 13
  _____

12) 128
  − 120
  _____

13) 153
  − 150
  _____

14) 136
  − 110
  _____

15) 144
  − 11
  _____

16) 153
  − 47
  _____

17) 173
  − 147
  _____

18) 130
  − 51
  _____

19) 153
  − 71
  _____

20) 169
  − 62
  _____

21) 114
  − 112
  _____

22) 172
  − 72
  _____

23) 165
  − 63
  _____

24) 156
  − 62
  _____

25) 159
  − 66
  _____

26) 159
  − 59
  _____

27) 131
  − 31
  _____

28) 135
  − 80
  _____

29) 126
  − 96
  _____

30) 157
  − 123
  _____

Time: :

Score:

Subtraction 0-1000

Subtract these 3 digit numbers.

1) 103 − 102

2) 562 − 148

3) 241 − 123

4) 553 − 332

5) 288 − 275

6) 582 − 441

7) 282 − 175

8) 953 − 539

9) 692 − 371

10) 635 − 392

11) 561 − 154

12) 715 − 490

13) 243 − 207

14) 898 − 837

15) 554 − 102

16) 768 − 524

17) 890 − 587

18) 808 − 283

19) 414 − 407

20) 718 − 185

21) 353 − 235

22) 881 − 209

23) 331 − 256

24) 886 − 147

25) 129 − 105

26) 287 − 126

27) 883 − 880

28) 912 − 820

29) 858 − 766

30) 951 − 446

Score:

Subtract these 3 digit numbers.

1)
```
    4,444
  − 3,733
```

2)
```
    7,717
  − 3,435
```

3)
```
    8,160
  − 7,570
```

4)
```
    2,406
  − 2,385
```

5)
```
    3,905
  − 3,842
```

6)
```
    3,747
  − 1,082
```

7)
```
    4,064
  − 3,723
```

8)
```
    7,580
  − 2,901
```

9)
```
    6,989
  − 3,946
```

10)
```
    2,108
  −   940
```

11)
```
    3,437
  − 2,607
```

12)
```
    3,361
  − 2,383
```

13)
```
    2,304
  − 1,100
```

14)
```
    6,736
  − 2,698
```

15)
```
    6,044
  − 5,936
```

16)
```
    8,406
  − 4,096
```

17)
```
    3,207
  − 3,191
```

18)
```
    3,447
  −   628
```

19)
```
    6,663
  −   876
```

20)
```
    6,166
  − 2,084
```

21)
```
    6,155
  − 2,873
```

22)
```
    8,032
  −   620
```

23)
```
    626
  − 226
```

24)
```
    9,002
  − 7,589
```

25)
```
    2,535
  − 1,385
```

Score:

Word Questions

Solve these subtraction word problems.

1) Michelle is collecting stamps, she has 140 stamps in total. She gives 88 stamps to another collector. How many stamps does Michelle have left?

2) There are 178 red and yellow flowers in a garden. 98 flowers are red. How many are yellow?

3) There are 130 boxes of chocolate in a supermarket. At Christmas, 112 boxes are bought by shoppers. How many are left after the Christmas sales?

4) In a school, there are 126 children in total in Year 3 and Year 4. 114 children are in Year 3. How many children are in Year 4?

5) Paul is sprinting and sprints 163 metres. After 1 minute he has sprinted 130 metres. How many metres are left?

Calculate the following mentally. See how fast you can finish the page.

150s

1) 56 + 19 = _____

2) 90 − 8 = _____

3) 66 + 77 = _____

4) 66 + 93 = _____

5) 73 − 43 = _____

6) 51 − 25 = _____

7) 97 − 10 = _____

8) 83 + 71 = _____

9) 95 − 88 = _____

10) 65 − 54 = _____

11) 80 + 5 = _____

12) 66 − 32 = _____

13) 89 − 84 = _____

14) 64 + 54 = _____

15) 70 − 69 = _____

16) 65 − 55 = _____

17) 62 + 62 = _____

18) 9 + 8 = _____

19) 91 − 26 = _____

20) 47 + 18 = _____

21) 60 − 45 = _____

22) 61 + 60 = _____

23) 67 − 60 = _____

24) 2 + 67 = _____

25) 20 + 79 = _____

26) 98 − 86 = _____

27) 62 − 5 = _____

28) 51 + 58 = _____

29) 44 + 65 = _____

30) 63 + 75 = _____

Time: :

Score:

Calculate the following.

1)
```
   516
 + 540
```

2)
```
   339
 − 220
```

3)
```
   414
 + 334
```

4)
```
   611
 − 607
```

5)
```
   473
 + 292
```

6)
```
   907
 + 636
```

7)
```
   164
 + 771
```

8)
```
   117
 − 114
```

9)
```
   327
 − 201
```

10)
```
   488
 − 193
```

11)
```
   258
 + 866
```

12)
```
   191
 − 173
```

☐ (12)

Shade the two correct sums.

1)

a) 341 + 151 = 482

b) 97.2 - 93 = 190.2

c) 154 + 102.4 = 256.4

d) 214 - 101 = 123

e) 84 + 68.4 = 152.4

☐ (2)

Score:

26

Solve these multiplication problems in your head.

60s

1) 4 × 2 = _____

2) 7 × 5 = _____

3) 12 × 9 = _____

4) 6 × 0 = _____

5) 3 × 7 = _____

6) 6 × 2 = _____

7) 7 × 9 = _____

8) 3 × 1 = _____

9) 2 × 4 = _____

10) 9 × 2 = _____

11) 10 × 8 = _____

12) 10 × 5 = _____

13) 10 × 9 = _____

14) 1 × 6 = _____

15) 3 × 4 = _____

16) 11 × 4 = _____

17) 10 × 12 = _____

18) 11 × 10 = _____

19) 8 × 4 = _____

20) 12 × 4 = _____

21) 10 × 3 = _____

22) 7 × 12 = _____

23) 4 × 6 = _____

24) 11 × 11 = _____

25) 4 × 10 = _____

26) 7 × 4 = _____

27) 11 × 2 = _____

28) 3 × 6 = _____

29) 6 × 1 = _____

30) 10 × 4 = _____

Time: :

Score:

Multiplication 2

Solve these multiplication problems in your head.

60s

1) $10 \times 12 = $_____

2) $3 \times 2 = $_____

3) $5 \times 11 = $_____

4) $5 \times 3 = $_____

5) $5 \times 6 = $_____

6) $11 \times 7 = $_____

7) $0 \times 11 = $_____

8) $7 \times 10 = $_____

9) $5 \times 7 = $_____

10) $2 \times 9 = $_____

11) $4 \times 1 = $_____

12) $12 \times 12 = $_____

13) $1 \times 6 = $_____

14) $10 \times 9 = $_____

15) $5 \times 4 = $_____

16) $2 \times 10 = $_____

17) $9 \times 2 = $_____

18) $1 \times 5 = $_____

19) $1 \times 8 = $_____

20) $6 \times 10 = $_____

21) $11 \times 12 = $_____

22) $4 \times 0 = $_____

23) $7 \times 5 = $_____

24) $1 \times 11 = $_____

25) $11 \times 1 = $_____

26) $11 \times 10 = $_____

27) $0 \times 3 = $_____

28) $9 \times 10 = $_____

29) $2 \times 11 = $_____

30) $8 \times 2 = $_____

Time: :

Score:

Add the missing values for these multiplications.

1) $1 \times \underline{\hphantom{XXX}} = 11$

2) $\underline{\hphantom{XXX}} \times 12 = 96$

3) $10 \times \underline{\hphantom{XXX}} = 80$

4) $4 \times 7 = \underline{\hphantom{XXX}}$

5) $\underline{\hphantom{XXX}} \times 1 = 1$

6) $\underline{\hphantom{XXX}} \times 8 = 72$

7) $\underline{\hphantom{XXX}} \times 10 = 110$

8) $\underline{\hphantom{XXX}} \times 11 = 77$

9) $11 \times 4 = \underline{\hphantom{XXX}}$

10) $10 \times \underline{\hphantom{XXX}} = 30$

11) $3 \times 2 = \underline{\hphantom{XXX}}$

12) $9 \times \underline{\hphantom{XXX}} = 99$

13) $6 \times 12 = \underline{\hphantom{XXX}}$

14) $8 \times 5 = \underline{\hphantom{XXX}}$

15) $\underline{\hphantom{XXX}} \times 5 = 55$

16) $4 \times \underline{\hphantom{XXX}} = 36$

17) $\underline{\hphantom{XXX}} \times 7 = 63$

18) $\underline{\hphantom{XXX}} \times 12 = 132$

19) $\underline{\hphantom{XXX}} \times 11 = 66$

20) $7 \times \underline{\hphantom{XXX}} = 28$

21) $7 \times 2 = \underline{\hphantom{XXX}}$

22) $1 \times \underline{\hphantom{XXX}} = 8$

23) $\underline{\hphantom{XXX}} \times 8 = 40$

24) $1 \times \underline{\hphantom{XXX}} = 10$

25) $8 \times 8 = \underline{\hphantom{XXX}}$

26) $\underline{\hphantom{XXX}} \times 8 = 0$

27) $7 \times \underline{\hphantom{XXX}} = 70$

28) $2 \times \underline{\hphantom{XXX}} = 18$

29) $6 \times \underline{\hphantom{XXX}} = 60$

30) $8 \times 3 = \underline{\hphantom{XXX}}$

Score:

Multiplying 3 Numbers

Answer the questions, multiplying out 3 numbers.

1) $10 \times 12 \times 7 =$ _____

2) $8 \times 8 \times 8 =$ _____

3) $10 \times 11 \times 9 =$ _____

4) $4 \times 12 \times 9 =$ _____

5) $3 \times 4 \times 3 =$ _____

6) $1 \times 12 \times 3 =$ _____

7) $5 \times 12 \times 7 =$ _____

8) $1 \times 11 \times 6 =$ _____

9) $8 \times 11 \times 6 =$ _____

10) $7 \times 5 \times 9 =$ _____

11) $8 \times 6 \times 1 =$ _____

12) $1 \times 9 \times 11 =$ _____

13) $8 \times 2 \times 8 =$ _____

14) $2 \times 6 \times 3 =$ _____

15) $4 \times 8 \times 7 =$ _____

16) $6 \times 6 \times 8 =$ _____

17) $8 \times 2 \times 4 =$ _____

18) $5 \times 11 \times 3 =$ _____

19) $9 \times 9 \times 2 =$ _____

20) $1 \times 12 \times 9 =$ _____

Time: :

Score:

30

Table Drill

Complete these tables.

1)

✖	11	4	7	8	12
4	44				
9					
10					
2					
5			35		

2)

✖	1	12	8	3	7
6					
2		24			
8					
7			56		
12					

3)

✖	11	4	3	9	8
5	55				
6					
2					
11					
12		48			

4)

✖	8	1	9	10	11
2					
7		7		70	
10					
5					
3					

Score:

Counting Patterns

Complete the counting tables.

1) Count by 5 from 0 to 45

		10							45

2) Count by 16 from 0 to 144

	16								144

3) Count by 24 from 0 to 216

		48					168		

☐

(3)

Shade the correct answer.

1)

$$\boxed{12}$$
×
$$\boxed{11}$$
=

(131)   (144)   (128)

(132)   (121)

2)

$$\boxed{17}$$
×
$$\boxed{12}$$
=

(210)   (200)   (205)

(206)   (204)

☐

(2)

Score:

32

Column Multiplication

Step 1: Multiply the 1's: 9x6=54. Write 4 in the 1's column and 5 (10s) under the 10s column.

Step 2: Multiply the 10's: 6x6=36. Add the additional 5 (36+5 = 41) from the 1's column 'carried' over to get your final answer.

1)
$$\begin{array}{r} 69 \\ \times\ 6 \\ \hline 414 \\ \hline \end{array}$$
5

2)
$$\begin{array}{r} 46 \\ \times\ 3 \\ \hline \end{array}$$

3)
$$\begin{array}{r} 24 \\ \times\ 7 \\ \hline \end{array}$$

4)
$$\begin{array}{r} 22 \\ \times\ 6 \\ \hline \end{array}$$

5)
$$\begin{array}{r} 85 \\ \times\ 9 \\ \hline \end{array}$$

6)
$$\begin{array}{r} 90 \\ \times\ 2 \\ \hline \end{array}$$

7)
$$\begin{array}{r} 77 \\ \times\ 2 \\ \hline \end{array}$$

8)
$$\begin{array}{r} 51 \\ \times\ 9 \\ \hline \end{array}$$

9)
$$\begin{array}{r} 64 \\ \times\ 5 \\ \hline \end{array}$$

10)
$$\begin{array}{r} 39 \\ \times\ 3 \\ \hline \end{array}$$

11)
$$\begin{array}{r} 66 \\ \times\ 5 \\ \hline \end{array}$$

12)
$$\begin{array}{r} 30 \\ \times\ 6 \\ \hline \end{array}$$

13)
$$\begin{array}{r} 83 \\ \times\ 8 \\ \hline \end{array}$$

14)
$$\begin{array}{r} 97 \\ \times\ 2 \\ \hline \end{array}$$

15)
$$\begin{array}{r} 63 \\ \times\ 7 \\ \hline \end{array}$$

16)
$$\begin{array}{r} 23 \\ \times\ 6 \\ \hline \end{array}$$

17)
$$\begin{array}{r} 43 \\ \times\ 3 \\ \hline \end{array}$$

18)
$$\begin{array}{r} 31 \\ \times\ 7 \\ \hline \end{array}$$

19)
$$\begin{array}{r} 31 \\ \times\ 2 \\ \hline \end{array}$$

20)
$$\begin{array}{r} 57 \\ \times\ 9 \\ \hline \end{array}$$

Score:

Column Multiplication 2

Step 1: Multiply the 1's: 6x6=36. Write 6 in the 1's column and 3 (10s) under the 10s column.

Step 2: Multiply the 10's: 4x6=24. Add the additional 3 carried over (24+3 = 27). Add the 7 in the 10's column and carry the 2 over.

Step 3: Multiply the 100's: 3x6=18. Add the additional 2 carried over (18+2=20). Add the 20 to get your final answer.

1)
$$\begin{array}{r} 346 \\ \times\ 6 \\ \hline 2076 \\ {\scriptstyle 2\ 3} \end{array}$$

2)
$$\begin{array}{r} 980 \\ \times\ 9 \\ \hline \end{array}$$

3)
$$\begin{array}{r} 166 \\ \times\ 8 \\ \hline \end{array}$$

4)
$$\begin{array}{r} 782 \\ \times\ 7 \\ \hline \end{array}$$

5)
$$\begin{array}{r} 232 \\ \times\ 8 \\ \hline \end{array}$$

6)
$$\begin{array}{r} 531 \\ \times\ 7 \\ \hline \end{array}$$

7)
$$\begin{array}{r} 400 \\ \times\ 3 \\ \hline \end{array}$$

8)
$$\begin{array}{r} 766 \\ \times\ 8 \\ \hline \end{array}$$

9)
$$\begin{array}{r} 22 \\ \times\ 7 \\ \hline \end{array}$$

10)
$$\begin{array}{r} 957 \\ \times\ 9 \\ \hline \end{array}$$

11)
$$\begin{array}{r} 473 \\ \times\ 7 \\ \hline \end{array}$$

12)
$$\begin{array}{r} 585 \\ \times\ 9 \\ \hline \end{array}$$

13)
$$\begin{array}{r} 931 \\ \times\ 6 \\ \hline \end{array}$$

14)
$$\begin{array}{r} 69 \\ \times\ 5 \\ \hline \end{array}$$

15)
$$\begin{array}{r} 535 \\ \times\ 5 \\ \hline \end{array}$$

16)
$$\begin{array}{r} 716 \\ \times\ 4 \\ \hline \end{array}$$

17)
$$\begin{array}{r} 742 \\ \times\ 2 \\ \hline \end{array}$$

18)
$$\begin{array}{r} 158 \\ \times\ 8 \\ \hline \end{array}$$

19)
$$\begin{array}{r} 467 \\ \times\ 2 \\ \hline \end{array}$$

20)
$$\begin{array}{r} 126 \\ \times\ 5 \\ \hline \end{array}$$

Score:

Complete the diamond problems. The top cell contains the product of the number in the right and left cells and the bottom cell contains the sum.
The first one has been done.

1)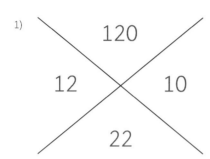

2)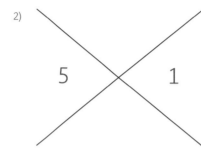

3)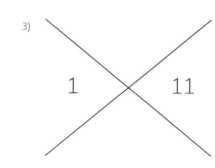

4)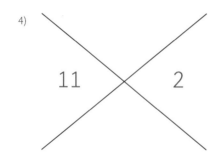

5)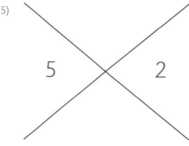

6)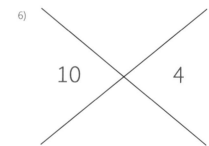

7)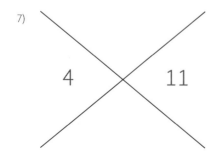

8)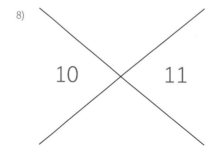

9)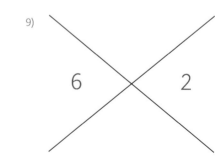

Score:

Fill in these multiplication boxes. Each row, column and diagonal can be multiplied to make the outer numbers.

1)

		196
		7	28
7	7		49
			144
28	168	42	42

2)

		63
3			27
	3		36
7			70
84	18	45	45

3)

		6
			7
	2	6	36
	3		36
63	6	24	56

4)

		105
			35
6			18
	6	4	120
150	18	28	60

5)

		14
2	3		42
	1		15
			48
20	12	126	12

6)

		42
	4		56
	6	3	90
			8
10	48	84	48

Score:

Division 0-12

Solve these division problems in your head.

1) $27 \div 3 =$ _____

2) $81 \div 9 =$ _____

3) $6 \div 2 =$ _____

4) $63 \div 7 =$ _____

5) $21 \div 7 =$ _____

6) $6 \div 1 =$ _____

7) $33 \div 3 =$ _____

8) $9 \div 1 =$ _____

9) $66 \div 6 =$ _____

10) $40 \div 10 =$ _____

11) $25 \div 5 =$ _____

12) $60 \div 10 =$ _____

13) $18 \div 6 =$ _____

14) $56 \div 7 =$ _____

15) $20 \div 2 =$ _____

16) $72 \div 9 =$ _____

17) $40 \div 4 =$ _____

18) $44 \div 4 =$ _____

19) $15 \div 5 =$ _____

20) $20 \div 5 =$ _____

21) $12 \div 3 =$ _____

22) $8 \div 8 =$ _____

23) $60 \div 6 =$ _____

24) $30 \div 5 =$ _____

25) $88 \div 11 =$ _____

26) $45 \div 9 =$ _____

27) $63 \div 9 =$ _____

28) $24 \div 8 =$ _____

29) $42 \div 6 =$ _____

30) $22 \div 11 =$ _____

Score:

Division Word Questions

1) Michael is baking cupcakes for a summer cake sale. He bakes 120 cupcakes and shares them equally between 15 stalls. How many cupcakes were given to each stall?

2) A football team scores 96 goals in the season across 32 games. How many goals do they score per game on average? (Goals divide by games).

3) Frank is a detectorist. With his metal detector he finds 12 roman coins in the ground. The coins have a combined total value of £240. If each coin is of equal value, how much is each coin worth?

(3)

True or False?

1) $120 \div 8$ and $150 \div 9$ are equal to the same number.

2) Dividing by 1 will always equal the divided number.

3) It is possible to divide numbers that have decimal places. e.g.. $54 \div 10.4$

(3)

Score:

Add the missing value.

1) $9 \div \underline{\qquad} = 1$

2) $55 \div \underline{\qquad} = 5$

3) $77 \div \underline{\qquad} = 7$

4) $66 \div \underline{\qquad} = 11$

5) $54 \div \underline{\qquad} = 6$

6) $\underline{\qquad} \div 9 = 2$

7) $4 \div \underline{\qquad} = 2$

8) $70 \div 7 = \underline{\qquad}$

9) $16 \div 2 = \underline{\qquad}$

10) $10 \div \underline{\qquad} = 2$

11) $72 \div 9 = \underline{\qquad}$

12) $2 \div \underline{\qquad} = 2$

13) $\underline{\qquad} \div 10 = 9$

14) $60 \div 6 = \underline{\qquad}$

15) $40 \div \underline{\qquad} = 8$

16) $70 \div 10 = \underline{\qquad}$

17) $12 \div 2 = \underline{\qquad}$

18) $54 \div 6 = \underline{\qquad}$

19) $84 \div 12 = \underline{\qquad}$

20) $7 \div 1 = \underline{\qquad}$

21) $32 \div 4 = \underline{\qquad}$

22) $45 \div 9 = \underline{\qquad}$

23) $42 \div 6 = \underline{\qquad}$

24) $14 \div 7 = \underline{\qquad}$

25) $40 \div 4 = \underline{\qquad}$

26) $55 \div 5 = \underline{\qquad}$

27) $77 \div 7 = \underline{\qquad}$

28) $2 \div 2 = \underline{\qquad}$

29) $35 \div 7 = \underline{\qquad}$

30) $6 \div 3 = \underline{\qquad}$

Score:

Remainders

Division with remainders: Sometimes when dividing there is a number left over, this is called a remainder.

Example: There are 7 bones to shares with 2 dogs.

7 cannot be divided into 2, so each dog would have 3 bones and there would be one left over.

This would be written as follows: $7 \div 2 = 3 \, r \, 1$

Answer these question with remainders. One is done for you.

1) $118 \div 10 = \underline{11 \, r \, 8}$ 　　2) $98 \div 6 = \underline{\hspace{2cm}}$ 　　3) $133 \div 6 = \underline{\hspace{2cm}}$

4) $16 \div 5 = \underline{\hspace{2cm}}$ 　　5) $35 \div 4 = \underline{\hspace{2cm}}$ 　　6) $111 \div 10 = \underline{\hspace{2cm}}$

7) $38 \div 5 = \underline{\hspace{2cm}}$ 　　8) $109 \div 11 = \underline{\hspace{2cm}}$ 　　9) $48 \div 5 = \underline{\hspace{2cm}}$

10) $17 \div 12 = \underline{\hspace{2cm}}$ 　　11) $65 \div 12 = \underline{\hspace{2cm}}$ 　　12) $41 \div 8 = \underline{\hspace{2cm}}$

13) $69 \div 7 = \underline{\hspace{2cm}}$ 　　14) $102 \div 3 = \underline{\hspace{2cm}}$ 　　15) $65 \div 9 = \underline{\hspace{2cm}}$

Score:

Factors are numbers that be multiplied by another to make a whole number.
List the factors for the numbers below, the first is done for you.

1) 35 _____ 1, 5 , 7, 35 _____

2) 95 _____

3) 32 _____

4) 27 _____

5) 14 _____

6) 51 _____

7) 97 _____

8) 4 _____

9) 91 _____

10) 18 _____

11) 89 _____

12) 94 _____

Common Factors are numbers that are multiples of two numbers.
List the factors for the multiples below, adding common factors in the centre
of the Venn diagram.

(11)

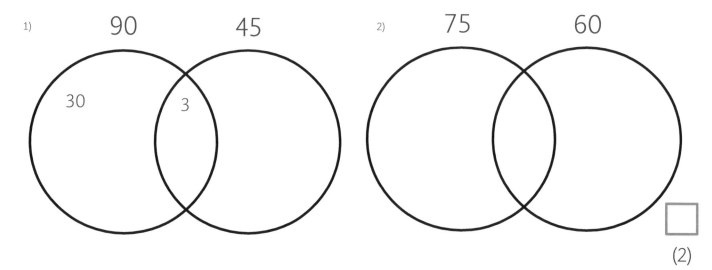

1) 90   45

30   3

2) 75   60

(2)

Score:

Multiples

A multiple is a number that can be divided by another number with no remainder. List the first five for each of the questions below, one is done for you.

1) 19 ___19, 38, 57, 76, 95___

2) 16 _____

3) 20 _____

4) 17 _____

5) 4 _____

6) 7 _____

7) 9 _____

8) 5 _____

9) 8 _____

10) 15 _____

11) 14 _____

12) 12 _____

(11)

Common multiples are numbers that can be divided by two numbers (again with no remainder). Write down the first six multiples for these numbers, adding common multiples in the centre of the Venn diagram.

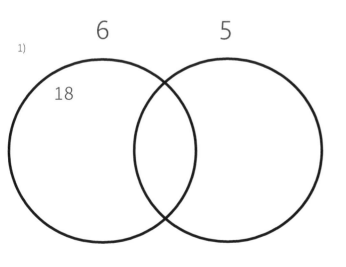

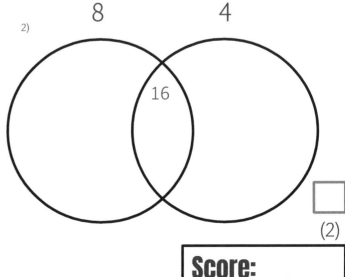

(2)

Score:

Identify the Fraction as per the shaded rectangles.

1) 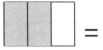 = $\dfrac{2}{3}$

2) 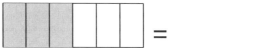 =

3)  =

4)  =

5) 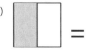 =

6) 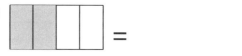 =

7)  =

8)  =

9)  =

10) 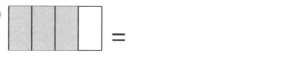 =

11)  =

12) 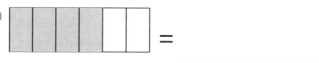 =

13) 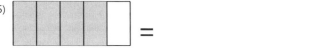 =

14)  =

15) 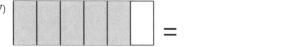 =

16)  =

17) 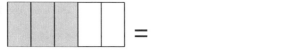 =

18) =

19) =

20) =

Score:

Identifying Fractions 2

Identify the fraction as per these shaded blocks of 10 by 10. Simplify when necessary.

1) 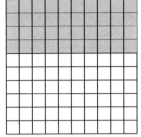 = $\dfrac{2}{5}$

2) 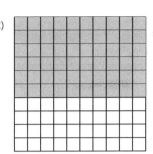 = _____

3) 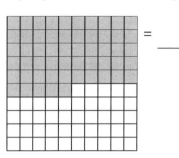 = _____

4) 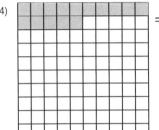 = _____

5) 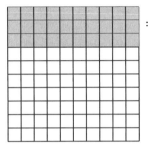 = _____

6) 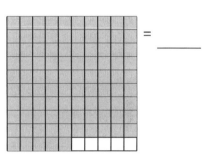 = _____

7) 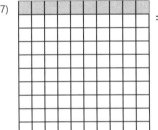 = _____

8) 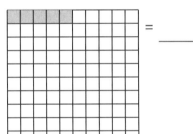 = _____

9) 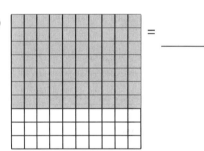 = _____

10) 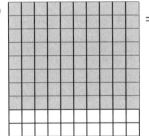 = _____

11) 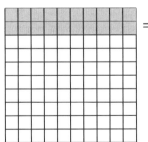 = _____

12) 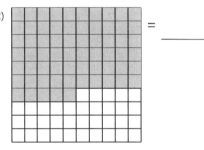 = _____

13) 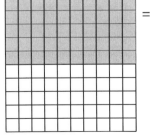 = _____

14) 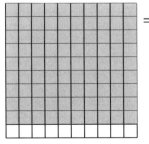 = _____

15) 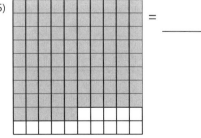 = _____

Score:

Answer these questions, writing the answer as a simplified top-heavy fraction.

1)
$$\frac{57}{100} + \frac{93}{100}$$
$$\frac{3}{2}$$
___

2)
$$\frac{41}{100} + \frac{63}{100}$$
___

3)
$$\frac{17}{100} + \frac{23}{100}$$
___

4)
$$\frac{21}{100} + \frac{87}{100}$$
___

5)
$$\frac{17}{100} + \frac{9}{100}$$
___

6)
$$\frac{23}{100} + \frac{83}{100}$$
___

7)
$$\frac{71}{100} + \frac{77}{100}$$
___

8)
$$\frac{63}{100} + \frac{87}{100}$$
___

9)
$$\frac{77}{100} + \frac{43}{100}$$
___

10)
$$\frac{27}{100} + \frac{3}{100}$$
___

11)
$$\frac{27}{100} + \frac{43}{100}$$
___

12)
$$\frac{89}{100} + \frac{1}{100}$$
___

13)
$$\frac{63}{100} + \frac{43}{100}$$
___

14)
$$\frac{17}{100} + \frac{27}{100}$$
___

15)
$$\frac{51}{100} + \frac{93}{100}$$
___

16)
$$\frac{3}{100} + \frac{99}{100}$$
___

Score:

Subtracting Fractions

Answer these questions and simplify.

1)
$$\frac{3}{4} - \frac{2}{4} = \frac{1}{4}$$

2)
$$\frac{19}{20} - \frac{13}{20}$$

3)
$$\frac{11}{25} - \frac{7}{25}$$

4)
$$\frac{99}{100} - \frac{98}{100}$$

5)
$$\frac{2}{3} - \frac{1}{3}$$

6)
$$\frac{3}{15} - \frac{1}{15}$$

7)
$$\frac{35}{50} - \frac{14}{50}$$

8)
$$\frac{7}{8} - \frac{6}{8}$$

9)
$$\frac{5}{6} - \frac{4}{6}$$

10)
$$\frac{3}{5} - \frac{2}{5}$$

11)
$$\frac{4}{6} - \frac{1}{6}$$

12)
$$\frac{10}{25} - \frac{2}{25}$$

13)
$$\frac{4}{5} - \frac{3}{5}$$

14)
$$\frac{8}{15} - \frac{5}{15}$$

15)
$$\frac{71}{100} - \frac{53}{100}$$

16)
$$\frac{7}{20} - \frac{2}{20}$$

17)
$$\frac{2}{4} - \frac{1}{4}$$

18)
$$\frac{7}{8} - \frac{4}{8}$$

19)
$$\frac{42}{50} - \frac{34}{50}$$

20)
$$\frac{42}{100} - \frac{14}{100}$$

Score:

Compare the fractions. Add <, > or =.

1) $\dfrac{8}{10} < \dfrac{9}{10}$ 2) $\dfrac{4}{5} \underline{\hphantom{<}} \dfrac{1}{5}$ 3) $\dfrac{1}{4} \underline{\hphantom{<}} \dfrac{2}{4}$ 4) $\dfrac{7}{10} \underline{\hphantom{<}} \dfrac{3}{10}$ 5) $\dfrac{1}{3} \underline{\hphantom{<}} \dfrac{2}{3}$

6) $\dfrac{1}{8} \underline{\hphantom{<}} \dfrac{7}{8}$ 7) $\dfrac{1}{2} \underline{\hphantom{<}} \dfrac{1}{2}$ 8) $\dfrac{4}{6} \underline{\hphantom{<}} \dfrac{3}{6}$ 9) $\dfrac{2}{4} \underline{\hphantom{<}} \dfrac{2}{4}$ 10) $\dfrac{6}{10} \underline{\hphantom{<}} \dfrac{8}{10}$

11) $\dfrac{2}{3} \underline{\hphantom{<}} \dfrac{1}{3}$ 12) $\dfrac{1}{6} \underline{\hphantom{<}} \dfrac{2}{6}$ 13) $\dfrac{4}{8} \underline{\hphantom{<}} \dfrac{3}{8}$ 14) $\dfrac{4}{5} \underline{\hphantom{<}} \dfrac{2}{5}$ 15) $\dfrac{2}{6} \underline{\hphantom{<}} \dfrac{4}{6}$

16) $\dfrac{6}{10} \underline{\hphantom{<}} \dfrac{3}{10}$ 17) $\dfrac{4}{8} \underline{\hphantom{<}} \dfrac{5}{8}$ 18) $\dfrac{3}{5} \underline{\hphantom{<}} \dfrac{4}{5}$ 19) $\dfrac{8}{10} \underline{\hphantom{<}} \dfrac{6}{10}$ 20) $\dfrac{6}{8} \underline{\hphantom{<}} \dfrac{4}{8}$

21) $\dfrac{3}{4} \underline{\hphantom{<}} \dfrac{2}{4}$ 22) $\dfrac{5}{6} \underline{\hphantom{<}} \dfrac{3}{6}$ 23) $\dfrac{1}{3} \underline{\hphantom{<}} \dfrac{1}{3}$ 24) $\dfrac{1}{5} \underline{\hphantom{<}} \dfrac{3}{5}$ 25) $\dfrac{7}{8} \underline{\hphantom{<}} \dfrac{3}{8}$

Score:

Fractions and Integers

Multiply these fractions and whole numbers.

1) $\frac{3}{8}$ of 8 = ___3___

2) $\frac{2}{4}$ of 4 = _____

3) $\frac{1}{3}$ of 3 = _____

4) $\frac{1}{5}$ of 5 = _____

5) $\frac{2}{6}$ of 6 = _____

6) $\frac{4}{6}$ of 6 = _____

7) $\frac{2}{5}$ of 5 = _____

8) $\frac{7}{8}$ of 8 = _____

9) $\frac{1}{4}$ of 4 = _____

10) $\frac{3}{6}$ of 6 = _____

11) $\frac{1}{3}$ of 6 = _____

12) $\frac{5}{8}$ of 8 = _____

13) $\frac{3}{4}$ of 4 = _____

14) $\frac{3}{5}$ of 5 = _____

15) $\frac{2}{3}$ of 3 = _____

16) $\frac{4}{8}$ of 8 = _____

17) $\frac{1}{6}$ of 6 = _____

18) $\frac{5}{6}$ of 6 = _____

19) $\frac{1}{8}$ of 8 = _____

20) $\frac{1}{4}$ of 8 = _____

21) $\frac{4}{5}$ of 5 = _____

22) $\frac{6}{8}$ of 8 = _____

23) $\frac{2}{3}$ of 6 = _____

24) $\frac{2}{8}$ of 8 = _____

25) $\frac{1}{3}$ of 9 = _____

26) $\frac{3}{4}$ of 8 = _____

27) $\frac{2}{4}$ of 8 = _____

28) $\frac{2}{3}$ of 9 = _____

29) $\frac{2}{8}$ of 8 = _____

30) $\frac{4}{5}$ of 5 = _____

Score:

Convert these fractions to decimals.

1) $\dfrac{15}{20} =$ ___0.75___

2) $\dfrac{3}{4} =$ _____

3) $\dfrac{3}{20} =$ _____

4) $\dfrac{3}{50} =$ _____

5) $\dfrac{7}{10} =$ _____

6) $\dfrac{4}{25} =$ _____

7) $\dfrac{1}{2} =$ _____

8) $\dfrac{3}{5} =$ _____

9) $\dfrac{30}{100} =$ _____

10) $\dfrac{75}{100} =$ _____

11) $\dfrac{5}{10} =$ _____

12) $\dfrac{9}{25} =$ _____

13) $\dfrac{9}{20} =$ _____

14) $\dfrac{81}{100} =$ _____

15) $\dfrac{1}{5} =$ _____

16) $\dfrac{1}{25} =$ _____

17) $\dfrac{1}{20} =$ _____

18) $\dfrac{6}{50} =$ _____

19) $\dfrac{15}{50} =$ _____

20) $\dfrac{57}{100} =$ _____

21) $\dfrac{2}{5} =$ _____

22) $\dfrac{5}{20} =$ _____

23) $\dfrac{5}{25} =$ _____

24) $\dfrac{6}{10} =$ _____

25) $\dfrac{11}{20} =$ _____

26) $\dfrac{8}{10} =$ _____

27) $\dfrac{1}{4} =$ _____

28) $\dfrac{45}{50} =$ _____

29) $\dfrac{3}{25} =$ _____

30) $\dfrac{4}{5} =$ _____

Score:

Decimals to Fractions

Convert these decimals to fractions (and simplify).

1) $0.53 = \dfrac{53}{100}$

2) $0.34 = $ _____

3) $0.7 = $ _____

4) $0.25 = $ _____

5) $0.5 = $ _____

6) $0.5 = $ _____

7) $0.8 = $ _____

8) $0.45 = $ _____

9) $0.75 = $ _____

10) $0.4 = $ _____

11) $0.04 = $ _____

12) $0.72 = $ _____

13) $0.52 = $ _____

14) $0.5 = $ _____

15) $0.48 = $ _____

16) $0.6 = $ _____

17) $0.35 = $ _____

18) $0.2 = $ _____

19) $0.72 = $ _____

20) $0.15 = $ _____

21) $0.12 = $ _____

22) $0.8 = $ _____

23) $0.31 = $ _____

24) $0.25 = $ _____

25) $0.58 = $ _____

26) $0.4 = $ _____

27) $0.37 = $ _____

28) $0.3 = $ _____

29) $0.88 = $ _____

30) $0.9 = $ _____

Score:

Solve these fraction division problems and simplify. A simple way of doing this is to flip the second fraction and multiply. An example with hints is given.

1) $\dfrac{3}{5} \div \dfrac{1}{5} = \dfrac{3}{5} \times \dfrac{5}{1} = \dfrac{15}{5} = \dfrac{3}{1} = 3$

2) $\dfrac{3}{6} \div \dfrac{3}{6} =$ _____

3) $\dfrac{4}{8} \div \dfrac{4}{8} =$ _____

4) $\dfrac{1}{3} \div \dfrac{2}{3} =$ _____

5) $\dfrac{1}{4} \div \dfrac{3}{4} =$ _____

6) $\dfrac{1}{4} \div \dfrac{1}{4} =$ _____

7) $\dfrac{3}{5} \div \dfrac{4}{5} =$ _____

8) $\dfrac{2}{3} \div \dfrac{2}{3} =$ _____

9) $\dfrac{4}{6} \div \dfrac{1}{6} =$ _____

10) $\dfrac{3}{8} \div \dfrac{6}{8} =$ _____

11) $\dfrac{3}{8} \div \dfrac{3}{8} =$ _____

12) $\dfrac{5}{6} \div \dfrac{5}{6} =$ _____

13) $\dfrac{2}{5} \div \dfrac{1}{5} =$ _____

14) $\dfrac{2}{6} \div \dfrac{3}{6} =$ _____

15) $\dfrac{4}{5} \div \dfrac{3}{5} =$ _____

16) $\dfrac{5}{8} \div \dfrac{7}{8} =$ _____

17) $\dfrac{2}{4} \div \dfrac{2}{4} =$ _____

18) $\dfrac{7}{8} \div \dfrac{4}{8} =$ _____

19) $\dfrac{1}{6} \div \dfrac{1}{6} =$ _____

20) $\dfrac{3}{4} \div \dfrac{1}{4} =$ _____

Score:

Rounding Decimals

Round to the underlined digit.

1) £<u>9</u>1.37 = _____£90.00_____

2) £80.5<u>4</u> = _____

3) £5.<u>8</u>6 = _____

4) £<u>4</u>4.34 = _____

5) £8<u>3</u>.76 = _____

6) £6<u>9</u>.06 = _____

7) £85.<u>1</u>4 = _____

8) £2<u>5</u>.79 = _____

9) £1.2<u>5</u> = _____

10) £43.8<u>1</u> = _____

11) £<u>0</u>.48 = _____

12) £92.5<u>8</u> = _____

13) £55.0<u>6</u> = _____

14) £21.9<u>7</u> = _____

15) £42.<u>4</u>0 = _____

16) £1<u>9</u>.11 = _____

17) £<u>9</u>0.19 = _____

18) £44.1<u>3</u> = _____

19) £<u>4</u>4.40 = _____

20) £2<u>1</u>.16 = _____

Score:

Solve these fractions word problems.

1) What is $\frac{4}{5}$ plus $\frac{2}{5}$?

2) What is the sum of $\frac{5}{8}$ and $\frac{2}{8}$?

3) A recipe calls for $\frac{2}{3}$ cups of white flour and $\frac{2}{3}$ cups of whole wheat flour. How many cups of flour in total is needed for the recipe?

4) If the sum of two fractions is $1\frac{1}{2}$ and the first fraction is $\frac{3}{4}$, what is the second fraction?

5) Paul ran $\frac{4}{8}$ of a mile and then walked another $\frac{6}{8}$ of a mile. How far did he travel?

6) Jackie cycled $\frac{1}{6}$ miles. She then stopped to have a snack. Then she cycled $\frac{5}{6}$ more miles. How far did Jackie cycle?

Score:

Solve these fractions word problems.

1) If you subtract $\frac{2}{4}$ from $\frac{3}{4}$ what is the result?

2) What is $\frac{2}{3}$ minus $\frac{1}{3}$?

3) Jake is working on a project that requires a piece of wire that is $\frac{2}{5}$ of a metre long. He has a longer piece of wire that he cuts and removes $\frac{2}{5}$ of a metre to make it the right size. How long was the original piece of wire?

4) Marin bought $\frac{5}{6}$ of a pound of raisins. After eating some of the raisins there was $\frac{1}{2}$ of a pound left over. How much did Marin already eat?

5) Allan bought $\frac{2}{3}$ of a pound of jelly beans. He ate $\frac{1}{3}$ of a pound. How much was left?

6) If you subtract $\frac{2}{4}$ from another fraction and the result is $\frac{1}{4}$, what was the other fraction?

Add the time for each clock.

1)

2)

3)

4)

5)

6)

7)

8)

9)

10)

11)

12)

13)

14)

15)

16)

Score:

Add the Clock Hands

Add the clock hands.

1)

4:58

2)

5:15

3)

3:11

4)

3:57

5)

12:12

6)

4:18

7)

2:29

8)

12:38

9)

10:40

10)

6:59

11)

10:12

12)

3:33

13)

2:58

14)

1:27

15)

5:48

16)

10:24

Score:

Convert the given measures of time.

1) 51 mins = <u>3,060 secs</u>

2) 65 hours = _____Mins

3) 51 days = ____Weeks____Days

4) 62 days = _____Hours

5) 77 hr = _____Days_____Hours

6) 76 secs = _____Mins_____Secs

7) 66 days = _____Hours

8) 32 secs = _____Mins_____Secs

9) 74 hours = _____Mins

10) 91 hours = _____Days_____Hours

11) 87 days = ____Weeks____Days

12) 81 min = _____Secs

13) 73 days = ____Weeks____Days

14) 12 hours = ____Days_____Hours

15) 76 days = _____Hours

16) 20 mins = _____Secs

17) 36 secs = _____Mins_____Secs

18) 27 mins = _____Mins

19) 58 hours = _____Mins

20) 18 hours = _____Mins

Score:

Time Machine

Convert these from 12 hour times to 24 hour times...and vice versa!

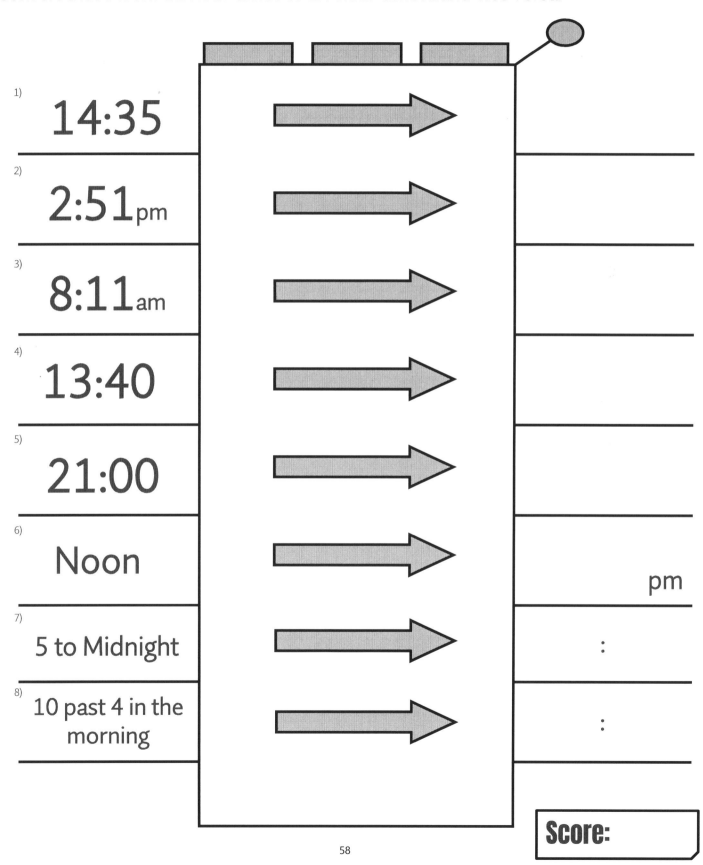

1) **14:35**

2) **2:51**pm

3) **8:11**am

4) **13:40**

5) **21:00**

6) Noon → _____ pm

7) 5 to Midnight → _____ :

8) 10 past 4 in the morning → _____ :

Score:

Draw the clock hands to show the passage of time.

1)

What time will it be in 3 hours 3 minutes?

2)

What time will it be in 2 hours 46 minutes?

3)

What time will it be in 2 hours?

4)

What time will it be in 3 hours 30 minutes?

5)

What time will it be in 4 hours 55 minutes?

6)

What time will it be in 1 hour 3 minutes?

7)

What time will it be in 5 hours 35 minutes?

8)

What time will it be in 4 hours 54 minutes?

Score:

Passage of Time 2

Draw the clock hands to show the passage of time.

1)

What time was it 2 hours 53 minutes ago?

2)

What time was it 5 hours 41 minutes ago?

3)

What time was it 1 hour 1 minute ago?

4)

What time was it 1 hour 4 minutes ago?

5)

What time was it 3 hours 28 minutes ago?

6)

What time was it 3 hours 52 minutes ago?

7)

What time was it 1 hour 15 minutes ago?

8)

What time was it 2 hours 59 minutes ago?

Score:

Use a ruler to measure these rectangles. Use the width and height to find the perimeter and area. (*The area is the width multiplied by the height, written in cm².*)

1)

Perimeter:

Area:

2)

Perimeter:

Area:

3)

Perimeter:

Area:

4)

Perimeter:

Area:

5)

Perimeter:

Area:

6)

Perimeter:

Area:

If the side of each small square is equal to 1cm. Find the perimeter and area of the shapes below.

1)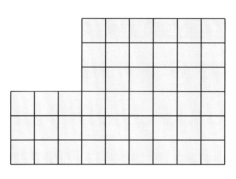

2)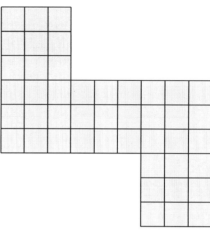

_____

3)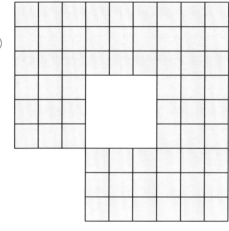

4)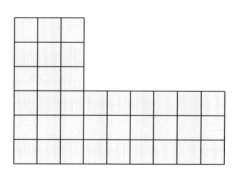

_____

5)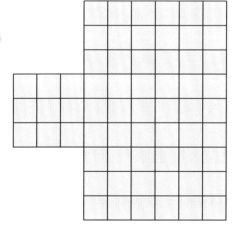

6)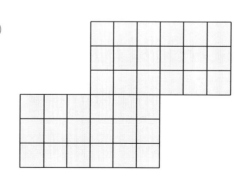

_____

Score:

Identify the temperature for each thermometer (in Celsius).

1) _____ °C

2) _____ °C

3) _____ °C

4) _____ °C

Shade the temperature for each thermometer (in Celsius).

1) __9__ °C

2) __-11__ °C

3) __17__ °C

4) __-28__ °C

Solve these word problems.

1) Zain pours 331ml of water into a 500ml jug. How much ml of space are left in the jug?

2) Liverpool are playing Manchester United and a ball has crossed the goal line by 11cm. Write this number in metres (as a decimal).

3) Lizzie has a pack of playing cards. Each card is 8cm x 5cm .

   a) What is the perimeter of each card?

   b) What is the area of each card?

   c) A harder question: In a pack of 52 playing cards. What number would you get if you totalled up all the perimeters and all the areas (each card is the same area and perimeter).

4) Dan has 210g of flour and divides into 15 equal parts. How many grams is each part?

Score:

Answer these questions. A list of possible answers is provided.

hot dog = £1.20	cola = £1.40
French-fries = £1.30	ice cream cone = £1.50
hamburger = £2.00	milk shake = £2.50
deluxe cheeseburger = £3.70	taco = £2.00

1)   Adam wants to buy a milk shake. How much will it cost him?

2)   Donald wants to buy a cola. How much will it cost him?

3)   If David buys a hot dog and an ice cream cone, how much money will he get back if he pays £10.00?

4)   If Jennifer wanted to buy an order of French-fries and a milk shake, how much would she have to pay?

5)   Audrey purchases a deluxe cheeseburger. How much money will she get back if she pays £10.00?

6)   Jackie purchases a hot dog, an order of French-fries, and a cola. What will her change be if she pays £10.00?

7)   What is the total cost of an ice cream cone and a cola?

8)   What is the total cost of a hamburger, an ice cream cone, and a cola?

9)   If Brian wanted to buy a milk shake, how much would he have to pay?

10)   What is the total cost of an order of French-fries and a cola?

A. £2.50   B. £2.50   C. £7.30   D. £2.90   E. £4.90   F. £6.10   G. £6.30
H. £3.80   I. £2.70   J. £1.40

Score:

65

Add the Coins

Add these coins together

1)

= _____

2)

= _____

3)

= _____

4)

= _____

5)

= _____

6)

= _____

7)

= _____

8)

= _____

9)

= _____

10)

= _____

11)

= _____

12)

= _____

Score:

Identify these regular polygons.

1)

2)

3)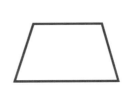

4)

5)

6)

7)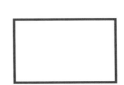

8)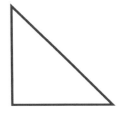

Identify these irregular polygons.

1)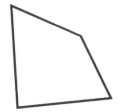

2)

3)

4)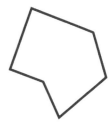

5)

6)

7)

8)

Score:

3-D Polgyons

Identify these 3-D polygons and the number of faces for each one.

1)

Name:

Faces:

2)

Name:

Faces:

3)

Name:

Faces:

4)

Name:

Faces:

5)

Name:

Faces:

6)

Name:

Faces:

Score:

Draw an irregular hexagon and an irregular octagon on the grid below.

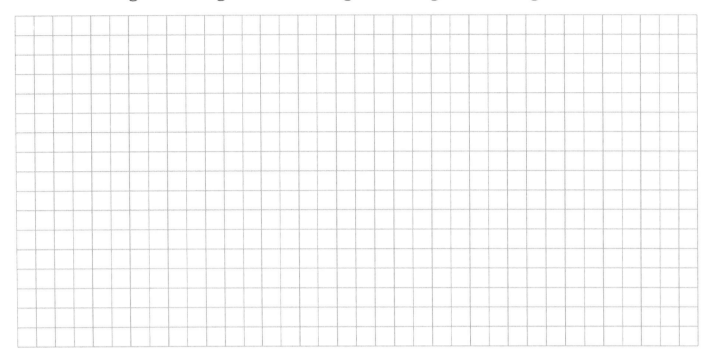

Defining Shapes

Pentagon

Hexagon

Nonagon

Triangle

Heptagon

Which of the above:

a) has the most sides;

b) has the least sides;

c) has both vertical and horizontal lines of symmetry?

Score:

How many symmetrical shapes can you draw on the graph paper below?

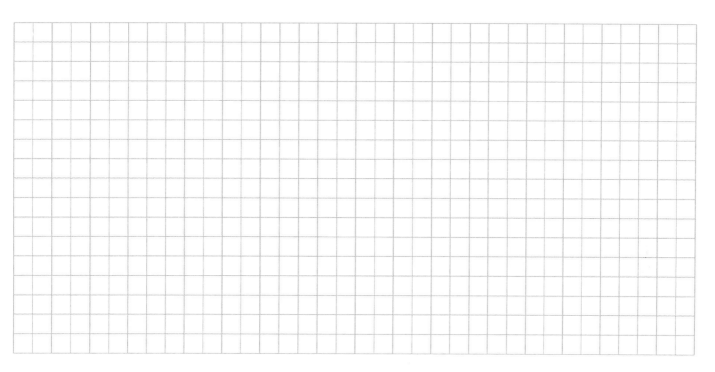

Lines of Symmetry

Which of the following contains two lines of symmetry?

Square
Rhombus
Parallelogram
Trapezium
Pentagon
Octagon

_____ and _____

Explain your answer.

_____

_____

_____

_____

_____

Score:

Which of the following is a right angle? Why is this?

1)

2)

3)
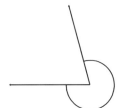

_____

(1)

Obtuse, acute or Reflex?

Look at the following angles and denote whether they are obtuse, acute or reflex angles. Explain your answer underneath.

1)

2)
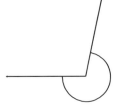

3)
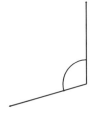

_____   _____   _____

_____

_____

(4)

Score:

Look at the following angles, have a go at ordering them from smallest to largest.

1)

2)

3)

4)

5)

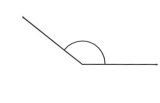

6)

On the graph paper below draw a right angle and an acute angle.

(1)

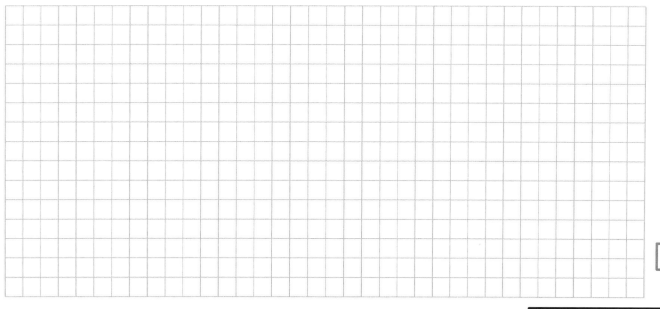

(2)

Score:

A treasure chest is lost at sea. Discover its coordinates following the instructions below and draw it on.

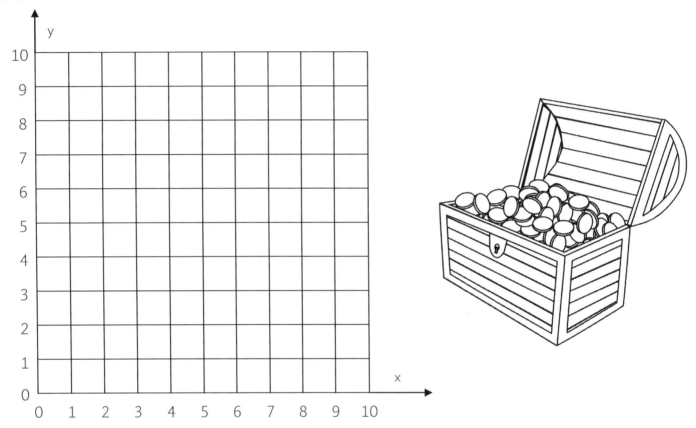

The difference between the x-coordinate and the y-coordinate is 5.

The x-coordinate is not divisible by 3, 5 or 7.

The y-coordinate is not an even number.

X multiplied by Y= 36

X+Y= 14.

(_____ , _____)

Draw the chest on the coordinates below. Now you've found it, you need your crew's help to uncover it.

They are currently at (6, 4). In the writing space below, write some instructions to help them find the quickest possible way to the chest.

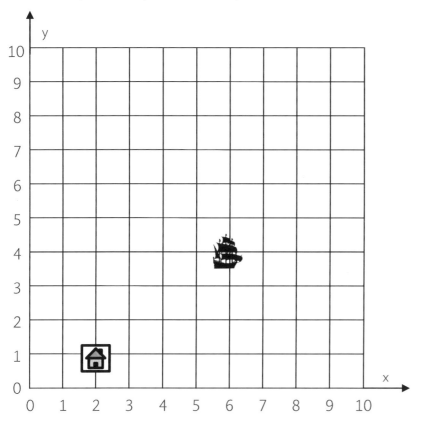

_____

_____

After finding the chest, the crew is now facing upwards. ⬆ They now want to get back to safer harbours at the point. (2,1) 🏠 Tell them which way to turn and then the directions back home.

Look at these grocery shop's apple sales. Then complete the bar chart adding in the graph title, axis titles and bars.

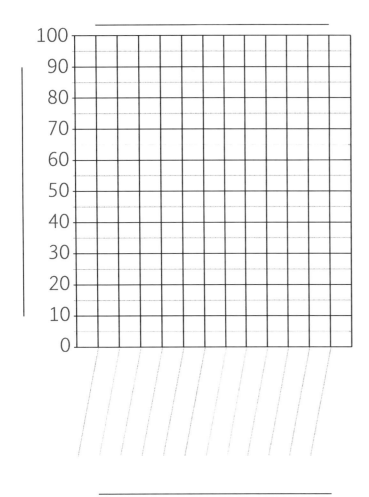

Apples Sold

Sales	Month
January	25
February	28
March	37
April	50
May	51
June	52
July	52
August	50
September	39
October	24
November	10
December	10

1) Which months had the most sales?

_____

2) Which month had the third least sales?

_____

3) How many sales were in October, November and December?

_____

4) How many months sold over 50 apples?

_____

5) From January to May, the shop owner sold twice as many oranges as apples. How many oranges did they sell in this time period?

_____

6) If the shop owner makes 50p per apple, how much money did they make in July and August?

_____

Score:

The pictogram below shows the number of animals in a zoo.

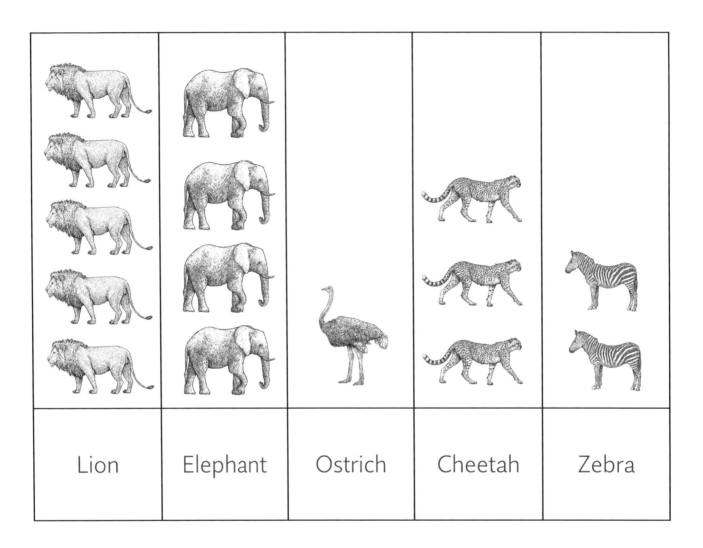

| Lion | Elephant | Ostrich | Cheetah | Zebra |

1) How many animals are there in total?

_____

2) What fraction of the total animals had four legs?

3) As a simplified fraction, how many of the animals had a mane?

_____

4) If you cubed the number of cheetahs how many would you have?

_____

5) There are 15 times the number of animals in the next zoo. How many are there at this zoo?

_____

6) How many tusks are in the zoo?

_____

Score:

Flights

Look at this line graph and table for the number of flights leaving an airport in one week.

1) Which day has the fourth most flights?

Day	Flights
Monday	121
Tuesday	250
Wednesday	157
Thursday	431
Friday	200
Saturday	510
Sunday	600

2) How many weekend flights were there?

3) What was the difference between Tuesday's and Saturday's number?

_____

4) How many weekday flights were there?

_____

5) Which days flight numbers were divisible by five?

_____

6) How many flights were on Wednesday and Thursday combined?

_____

7) On what day did the number of flights cross 1,000 flights for the week

_____

Score:

ANSWERS

Page 1: Counting on a Line 1

1.

Page 1: Counting on a Line 2

2.

Page 1: Counting on a Line 3

3.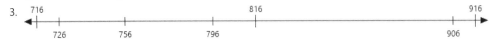

Page 1: Missing Bricks

1. Subtract 18: -33, -51, -69   2. Add 10: -65, -55, -45   3. Subtract 6: -89, -95, -101

Page 2: Counting Up and Down 1

1.

| 606 | 600 | 594 | 588 | 582 | 576 | 570 | 564 | 558 | 552 |

Page 2: Counting Up and Down 2

2.

| -7 | -6 | -5 | -4 | -3 | -2 | -1 | 0 | 1 | 2 |

Page 2: Counting Up and Down 3

3.

| 189 | 196 | 203 | 210 | 217 | 224 | 231 | 238 | 245 | 252 |

Page 2: Counting Up and Down 4

4.

| 306 | 297 | 288 | 279 | 270 | 261 | 252 | 243 | 234 | 225 |

Page 2: Counting Table

1. Count by 9 from 40 to 391

40	49	58	67	76	85	94	103	112	121
130	139	148	157	166	175	184	193	202	211
220	229	238	247	256	265	274	283	292	301
310	319	328	337	346	355	364	373	382	391

Page 3: Place Value

1. 4 tens   2. 4 hundreds   3. 1 ten   4. 5 thousands   5. 6 thousands   6. 4 thousands

7. 8 tens   8. 4 thousands   9. 7 tens   10. 4 thousands

Page 3: Partitioning

1. 7000 + 500 + 60 + 7   2. 8000 + 700 + 60 + 4   3. 4000 + 500 + 60 + 7

Page 4: Ordering Numbers: Smallest to Largest

1.		2.		3.		4.	
4,773	253	2,865	633	3,780	410	2,314	854
890	403	1,271	1,271	1,432	733	6,783	864
253	816	633	1,603	733	1,432	2,838	2,314
816	890	2,675	2,675	9,962	3,780	864	2,838
403	4,773	1,603	2,865	410	9,962	854	6,783

5.		6.	
6,186	363	999	411
519	391	5,995	999
363	519	411	4,015
788	788	4,015	5,995
391	6,186	7,727	7,727

Page 4: Ordering Numbers: Largest to Smallest

1.		2.		3.	
301	301	952	438	2,851	711
8,025	320	9,439	445	7,689	1,807
7,633	7,633	438	952	711	2,851
9,208	8,025	445	7,988	1,807	5,726
320	9,208	7,988	9,439	5,726	7,689

Page 5: Circle the smallest numbers

1.	2.	3.	4.	5.	6.	7.	8.
2,481	4,925	1,999	1,818	2,881	1,728	4,528	(42)
(161)	2,812	3,168	(1,490)	1,834	3,177	3,790	2,184
503	4,893	3,054	4,492	(229)	(193)	(1,520)	3,232
4,967	(855)	(874)	2,639	2,508	2,907	2,240	3,983
3,379	2,364	4,535	3,611	2,995	4,619	2,728	4,317

Page 5: Circle the largest numbers

1.	2.	3.	4.	5.	6.	7.	8.
(4,204)	(4,867)	1,721	646	1,747	3,209	(4,634)	3,737
4,144	2,959	1,429	(4,933)	2,619	1,647	3,258	329
1,505	4,666	1,133	2,995	1,986	813	509	(3,941)
1,289	1,363	2,495	1,972	1,237	3,146	3,322	3,779
3,729	3,674	(3,051)	1,651	(2,837)	(4,492)	4,407	3,129

Page 6: Circle the smallest and largest number

1.	2.	3.	4.	5.	6.	7.	8.
(2,404)	(426)	1,821	(3,772)	4,168	(4,567)	3,027	(735)
(401)	728	3,483	1,426	(4,238)	3,194	2,633	(3,253)
874	1,528	(4,615)	(83)	(1,840)	(1,394)	(3,798)	2,343
1,386	(3,738)	(1,104)	88	2,340	3,816	2,588	901
474	2,147	4,437	1,548	3,049	3,669	(1,470)	1,812

Page 6: Negatives: Circle the smallest and largest

1.	2.	3.	4.	5.	6.	7.	8.
1,306	-707	(-9,669)	-5,246	-344	391	(-9,048)	-294
536	-2,032	(2,568)	-3,526	-3,564	(-7,238)	-7,026	1,369
1,488	2,078	-6,219	(-9,197)	(-5,443)	-1,567	(2,649)	(-1,740)
(2,699)	(2,569)	-3,004	(357)	-4,385	-737	1,530	19
(-1,308)	(-3,757)	-2,292	-8,443	(2,119)	(2,940)	-1,353	(4,219)

Page 7: Numbers as Words

1. one hundred ten thousand six hundred and sixty-two

2. five hundred twenty-four thousand three hundred and thirty-two

3. three hundred twenty-four thousand eight hundred and forty-nine

4. two hundred thirteen thousand and seventy

5. eight hundred seventy-six thousand two hundred and thirty-four

Page 7: Words as Numbers

1. 8,908   2. 39,957   3. 63,544   4. 15,068   5. 56,453

Page 8: Before, After, Between

1. -1305   2. -2586 -2584   3. -1712 -1710   4. -9466 -9464   5. -8532 -8530   6. -3328

7. -1978 -1976   8. -5336   9. -4207   10. -2051

Page 8: Rounding Numbers

1. 3,840   2. 1,100   3. 2,000   4. 6,868   5. 9,800   6. 3,922   7. 4,590   8. 5,000   9. 1,350   10. 8,980

11. 4,900   12. 9,720

Page 9: Numbers to Roman Numerals

1. XIX   2. V   3. C   4. LXXVII   5. LXXXII   6. VI   7. LXXX   8. I   9. LIII   10. XXIV

11. LI   12. XXII   13. XLIX   14. XVI   15. XXXI

Page 10: Roman Numerals to Numbers

1. 93   2. 70   3. 4   4. 8   5. 10   6. 7   7. 6   8. 1   9. 21   10. 24   11. 5   12. 51   13. 54   14. 74

15. 88

Page 10: Roman Numeral Maths - Roman Numerals

1. XXII   2. IX   3. CVI   4. MC

Page 10: Roman Numeral Maths - Numbers

1. 9   2. 120

Page 11: Input Output

1.

Input	Output
107	153
39	85
41	87
172	218

Add 46

2.

Input	Output
141	190
4	53
89	138
101	150

Add 49

3.

Input	Output
172	215
200	243
176	219
94	137

Add 43

4.

Input	Output
57	137
79	159
126	206
152	232

Add 80

5. Input	Output
117	213
43	139
19	115
14	110

Add 96

6. Input	Output
61	97
165	201
170	206
11	47

Add 36

Page 11: Shade the correct answer

1. 89 + 621 = 710   2. 75 - 127 = -52

Page 12:   Table Drills

1.

+	22	14	52	26	97
834	856	848	886	860	931
657	679	671	709	683	754
340	362	354	392	366	437
225	247	239	277	251	322
588	610	602	640	614	685

2.

+	775	550	500	325	19
22	797	572	522	347	41
15	790	565	515	340	34
39	814	589	539	364	58
500	1,275	1,050	1,000	825	519
30	805	580	530	355	49

Page 12:   Shade the correct sum

1. The correct sum is c)

Page 13:   Number Bonds: Part 1

1. 19   2. 55   3. 11   4. 5   5. 30   6. 105   7. 96   8. 7   9. 104   10. 1   11. 75   12. 29   13. 104

14. 8   15. 34   16. 102   17. 52   18. 5   19. 57   20. -10   21. 57   22. 131   23. 11   24. 7   25. 12

Page 14:   Number Bonds: Part 2

1. 21   2. 56   3. 63   4. 81   5. 74   6. 85   7. 31   8. 111   9. 161   10. 41   11. 182   12. 119   13. 134

14. 75   15. 13   16. 167   17. 83   18. 142   19. 81   20. 47   21. 78   22. 35   23. 29   24. 67   25. 36   26. 95

27. 140   28. 66   29. 102   30. 94

Page 15:   Addition: 0-200

1. 162   2. 194   3. 156   4. 90   5. 118   6. 72   7. 190   8. 101   9. 191   10. 125   11. 91   12. 166   13. 132

14. 190   15. 101   16. 71   17. 82   18. 163   19. 191   20. 125   21. 169   22. 162   23. 106   24. 156   25. 155   26. 191

27. 165   28. 129   29. 124   30. 133

Page 16:   Addition: 0-500

1. 435   2. 404   3. 469   4. 329   5. 411   6. 467   7. 453   8. 275   9. 231   10. 472   11. 489   12. 415

13. 454   14. 421   15. 369   16. 270   17. 456   18. 425   19. 393   20. 451   21. 327   22. 318   23. 480   24. 458

25. 491   26. 226   27. 433   28. 448   29. 500   30. 215

Page 17:   Addition: 0-1000

1. 648   2. 573   3. 686   4. 665   5. 733   6. 537   7. 389   8. 419   9. 707   10. 749   11. 679   12. 458

13. 758   14. 741   15. 811   16. 592   17. 730   18. 732   19. 566   20. 859   21. 505   22. 515   23. 755   24. 428

25. 577   26. 752   27. 939   28. 734   29. 520   30. 512

Page 18: Addition: 0-10000

1. 6,644   2. 6,999   3. 5,113   4. 5,357   5. 3,678   6. 3,188   7. 5,828   8. 5,798   9. 3,597   10. 9,466

11. 4,825   12. 8,123   13. 2,108   14. 2,880   15. 5,595   16. 8,833   17. 5,008   18. 4,110   19. 6,156   20. 7,117

Page 19: Adding 3 Numbers

1. 89   2. 50   3. 71   4. 30   5. 99   6. 77   7. 94   8. 76   9. 96   10. 72   11. 79   12. 63   13. 65

14. 99   15. 93   16. 68   17. 59   18. 118   19. 73   20. 50

Page 20: Word Questions - Addition

1. 310   2. 352   3. 332   4. 352   5. 371   6. 374

Page 21: Subtraction 0-200

1. 28   2. 30   3. 31   4. 98   5. 143   6. 140   7. 50   8. 56   9. 19   10. 9   11. 129   12. 8   13. 3

14. 26   15. 133   16. 106   17. 26   18. 79   19. 82   20. 107   21. 2   22. 100   23. 102   24. 94   25. 93   26. 100

27. 100   28. 55   29. 30   30. 34

Page 22: Subtraction 0-1000

1. 1   2. 414   3. 118   4. 221   5. 13   6. 141   7. 107   8. 414   9. 321   10. 243   11. 407   12. 225

13. 36   14. 61   15. 452   16. 244   17. 303   18. 525   19. 7   20. 533   21. 118   22. 672   23. 75   24. 739

25. 24   26. 161   27. 3   28. 92   29. 92   30. 505

Page 23: Subtraction: 0-10000

1. 711   2. 4,282   3. 590   4. 21   5. 63   6. 2,665   7. 341   8. 4,679   9. 3,043   10. 1,168

11. 830   12. 978   13. 1,204   14. 4,038   15. 108   16. 4,310   17. 16   18. 2,819   19. 5,787   20. 4,082

21. 3,282   22. 7,412   23. 400   24. 1,413   25. 1,150

Page 24: Word Questions - Subtraction

1. 52   2. 80   3. 18   4. 12   5. 33

Page 25: Mixed Operations

1. 75   2. 82   3. 143   4. 159   5. 30   6. 26   7. 87   8. 154   9. 7   10. 11   11. 85   12. 34   13. 5

14. 118   15. 1   16. 10   17. 124   18. 17   19. 65   20. 65   21. 15   22. 121   23. 7   24. 69   25. 99   26. 12

27. 57   28. 109   29. 109   30. 138

Page 26: Mixed Operations 2

1. 1,056   2. 119   3. 748   4. 4   5. 765   6. 1,543   7. 935   8. 3   9. 126   10. 295   11. 1,124

12. 18

Page 26: Shade the 2 correct sums

1. The two correct sums are c) and e)

Page 27: Multiplication 1

1. 8   2. 35   3. 108   4. 0   5. 21   6. 12   7. 63   8. 3   9. 8   10. 18   11. 80   12. 50   13. 90

14. 6   15. 12   16. 44   17. 120   18. 110   19. 32   20. 48   21. 30   22. 84   23. 24   24. 121   25. 40   26. 28

27. 22   28. 18   29. 6   30. 40

Page 28: Multiplication 2

1. 120   2. 6   3. 55   4. 15   5. 30   6. 77   7. 0   8. 70   9. 35   10. 18   11. 4   12. 144

13. 6   14. 90   15. 20   16. 20   17. 18   18. 5   19. 8   20. 60   21. 132   22. 0   23. 35   24. 11

Page 29: Missing Value

1. 11   2. 8   3. 8   4. 28   5. 1   6. 9   7. 11   8. 7   9. 44   10. 3   11. 6   12. 11   13. 72   14. 40

15. 11   16. 9   17. 9   18. 11   19. 6   20. 4   21. 14   22. 8   23. 5   24. 10   25. 64   26. 0   27. 10   28. 9

29. 10   30. 24

Page 30: Multiplying 3 Numbers

1. 840   2. 512   3. 990   4. 432   5. 36   6. 36   7. 420   8. 66   9. 528   10. 315   11. 48   12. 99

13. 128   14. 36   15. 224   16. 288   17. 64   18. 165   19. 162   20. 108

Page 31: Table Drill

1.

×	11	4	7	8	12
4	44	16	28	32	48
9	99	36	63	72	108
10	110	40	70	80	120
2	22	8	14	16	24
5	55	20	35	40	60

2.

×	1	12	8	3	7
6	6	72	48	18	42
2	2	24	16	6	14
8	8	96	64	24	56
7	7	84	56	21	49
12	12	144	96	36	84

3.

×	11	4	3	9	8
5	55	20	15	45	40
6	66	24	18	54	48
2	22	8	6	18	16
11	121	44	33	99	88
12	132	48	36	108	96

4.

×	8	1	9	10	11
2	16	2	18	20	22
7	56	7	63	70	77
10	80	10	90	100	110
5	40	5	45	50	55
3	24	3	27	30	33

Page 32: Counting Patterns

1.

0	5	10	15	20	25	30	35	40	45

2.

0	16	32	48	64	80	96	112	128	144

3.

0	24	48	72	96	120	144	168	192	216

Page 32: Shade the correct answers

1. 132   2. 204

Page 33: Column Multiplication

1. 414   2. 138   3. 168   4. 132   5. 765   6. 180   7. 154   8. 459   9. 320   10. 117   11. 330   12. 180

13. 664   14. 194   15. 441   16. 138   17. 129   18. 217   19. 62   20. 513

Page 34: Column Multiplication 2

1. 2,076   2. 8,820   3. 1,328   4. 5,474   5. 1,856   6. 3,717   7. 1,200   8. 6,128   9. 154   10. 8,613

11. 3,311   12. 5,265   13. 5,586   14. 345   15. 2,675   16. 2,864   17. 1,484   18. 1,264   19. 934   20. 630

Page 35: Diamond Maths

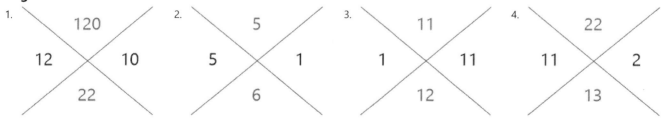

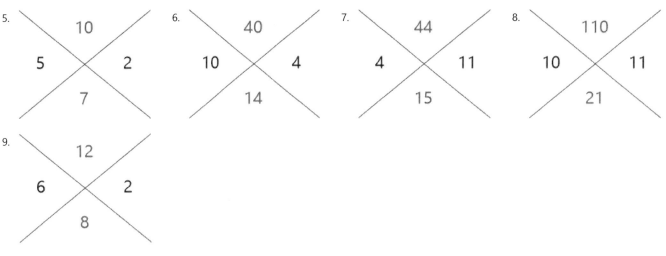

Page 36: Multiplication Boxes

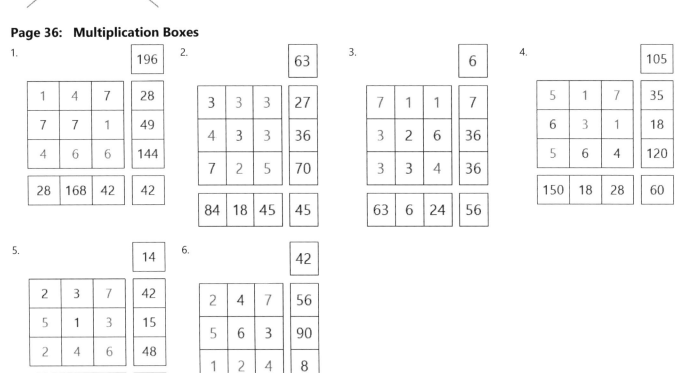

Page 37: Division 0-12

1. **9**   2. **9**   3. **3**   4. **9**   5. **3**   6. **6**   7. **11**   8. **9**   9. **11**   10. **4**   11. **5**   12. **6**   13. **3**   14. **8**

15. **10**   16. **8**   17. **10**   18. **11**   19. **3**   20. **4**   21. **4**   22. **1**   23. **10**   24. **6**   25. **8**   26. **5**   27. **7**   28. **3**

29. **7**   30. **2**

Page 38: Division Word Questions

1. **8 cupcakes**   2. **3 goals per game**   3. **Each coin is worth £20**

Page 38: True or False

1. False   2. True   3. True

Page 39: Missing Value

1. **9**   2. **11**   3. **11**   4. **6**   5. **9**   6. **18**   7. **2**   8. **10**   9. **8**   10. **5**   11. **8**   12. **1**   13. **90**   14. **10**

15. **5**   16. **7**   17. **6**   18. **9**   19. **7**   20. **7**   21. **8**   22. **5**   23. **7**   24. **2**   25. **10**   26. **11**   27. **11**   28. **1**

29. **5**   30. **2**

Page 40: Remainders

1. 11 R8   2. 16 R2   3. 22 R1   4. 3 R1   5. 8 R3   6. 11 R1   7. 7 R3   8. 9 R10   9. 9 R3   10. 1 R5

11. 5 R5   12. 5 R1   13. 9 R6   14. 34 R0   15. 7 R2

Page 41: Factors

1. 1, 5, 7, 35   2. 1, 5, 19, 95   3. 1, 2, 4, 8, 16, 32   4. 1, 3, 9, 27   5. 1, 2, 7, 14   6. 1, 3, 17, 51

7. 1, 97   8. 1, 2, 4   9. 1, 7, 13, 91   10. 1, 2, 3, 6, 9, 18   11. 1, 89   12. 1, 2, 47, 94

Page 41: Venn Diagram: Factors

1. 45: 1, 3, 5, 9, 15, 45   2. 75: 1, 3, 5, 15, 25, 75

90: 1, 2, 3, 5, 6, 9, 10, 15, 18, 30, 45, 90   60: 1, 2, 3, 4, 5, 6, 10, 12, 15, 20, 30, 60

Common Factors: 1, 3, 5, 9, 15, 45   Common factors: 1, 3, 5, 15

Page 42: Multiples

1. 19, 38, 57, 76, 95   2. 16, 32, 48, 64, 80   3. 20, 40, 60, 80, 100   4. 17, 34, 51, 68, 85   5. 4, 8, 12, 16, 20

6. 7, 14, 21, 28, 35   7. 9, 18, 27, 36, 45   8. 5, 10, 15, 20, 25   9. 8, 16, 24, 32, 40   10. 15, 30, 45, 60, 75

11. 14, 28, 42, 56, 70   12. 12, 24, 36, 48, 60

Page 42: Venn Diagram: Multiples

1. 6: 6, 12, 18, 24, 30, 36.   2. 8: 8, 16, 24, 32, 40, 48.

5: 5, 10, 15, 20, 25, 30.   4: 4, 8, 12, 16, 20, 24.

Common Multiple: 30   Common Multiples: 8, 16, 24.

Page 43: Identifying Fractions

1. 2/3   2. 1/4   3. 7/8   4. 3/6   5. 1/2   6. 6/8   7. 2/5   8. 2/4   9. 1/3   10. 2/6   11. 4/8   12. 3/4

13. 1/5   14. 4/6   15. 4/5   16. 2/8   17. 5/6   18. 5/8   19. 3/5   20. 3/8

Page 44: Identifying Fractions 2

1. 2/5   2. 3/5   3. 11/20   4. 3/20   5. 3/10   6. 19/20   7. 1/10   8. 1/20   9. 7/10   10. 4/5

11. 1/5   12. 13/20   13. 1/2   14. 9/10   15. 17/20

Page 45: Adding Fractions

1. 3/2   2. 26/25   3. 2/5   4. 27/25   5. 13/50   6. 53/50   7. 37/25   8. 3/2   9. 6/5   10. 3/10

11. 7/10   12. 9/10   13. 53/50   14. 11/25   15. 36/25   16. 51/50

Page 46: Subtracting Fractions

1. 1/4   2. 3/10   3. 4/25   4. 1/100   5. 1/3   6. 2/15   7. 21/50   8. 1/8   9. 1/6   10. 1/5   11. 1/2

12. 8/25   13. 1/5   14. 1/5   15. 9/50   16. 1/4   17. 1/4   18. 3/8   19. 4/25   20. 7/25

Page 47: Comparing Fractions

1. <   2. >   3. <   4. >   5. <   6. <   7. =   8. >   9. =   10. <   11. >   12. <   13. >   14. >   15. <   16. >

17. <   18. <   19. >   20. >   21. >   22. >   23. =   24. <   25. >

Page 48: Fractions and Integers

1. 3   2. 2   3. 1   4. 1   5. 2   6. 4   7. 2   8. 7   9. 1   10. 3   11. 2   12. 5   13. 3   14. 3   15. 2   16. 4

17. 1   18. 5   19. 1   20. 2   21. 4   22. 6   23. 4   24. 2   25. 3   26. 6   27. 4   28. 6   29. 2   30. 4

Page 49: Fractions to Decimals

1. 0.75   2. 0.75   3. 0.15   4. 0.06   5. 0.7   6. 0.16   7. 0.5   8. 0.6   9. 0.3   10. 0.75   11. 0.5

12. 0.36   13. 0.45   14. 0.81   15. 0.2   16. 0.04   17. 0.05   18. 0.12   19. 0.3   20. 0.57   21. 0.4   22. 0.25

23. 0.2   24. 0.6   25. 0.55   26. 0.8   27. 0.25   28. 0.9   29. 0.12   30. 0.8

Page 50:   Decimals to Fractions

1. 53/100   2. 17/50   3. 7/10   4. 5/20   5. 2/4   6. 1/2   7. 4/5   8. 9/20   9. 3/4

10. 2/5   11. 1/25   12. 72/100   13. 26/50   14. 5/10   15. 48/100   16. 30/50   17. 7/20   18. 2/10

19. 18/25   20. 3/20   21. 3/25   22. 8/10   23. 31/100   24. 1/4   25. 29/50   26. 4/10   27. 37/100

28. 6/20   29. 22/25   30. 45/50

Page 51:   Dividing Fractions

1. 3/1   2. 1/1   3. 1/1   4. 1/2   5. 1/3   6. 1/1   7. 3/4   8. 1/1   9. 4/1   10. 1/2   11. 1/1   12. 1/1   13. 2/1

14. 2/3   15. 4/3   16. 5/7   17. 1/1   18. 7/4   19. 1/1   20. 3/1

Page 52:   Rounding Decimals

1. £90.00   2. £80.54   3. £5.90   4. £40.00   5. £84.00   6. £69.00   7. £85.00   8. £26.00   9. £1.25

10. £43.81   11. £0.00   12. £92.58   13. £55.06   14. £21.97   15. £42.40   16. £19.00   17. £90.00   18. £44.13

19. £40.00   20. £21.00

Page 53:   Word Questions

1. 1 1/5   2. 7/8   3. 1 1/3   4. 3/4   5. 1 1/4   6. 1

Page 54:   Word Questions 2

1. 1/4   2. 1/3   3. 4/5   4. 2/6   5. 1/3   6. 3/4

Page 55:   Add the times

1. 5:22   2. 4:21   3. 4:58   4. 2:10   5. 9:33

6. 1:44   7. 9:06   8. 5:07   9. 2:05   10. 7:13

11. 4:06   12. 10:14   13. 6:19   14. 12:05   15. 8:23

16.

9:52

Page 56: Add the clock hands

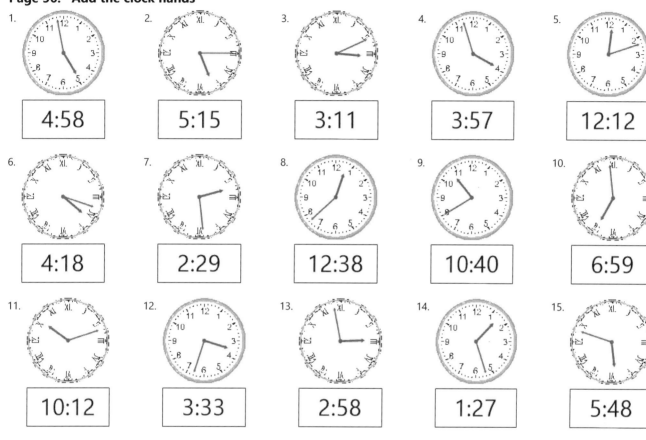

1.
4:58

2.
5:15

3.
3:11

4.
3:57

5.
12:12

6.
4:18

7.
2:29

8.
12:38

9.
10:40

10.
6:59

11.
10:12

12.
3:33

13.
2:58

14.
1:27

15.
5:48

16.

10:24

Page 57: Time Conversions

1. 3,060 sec
2. 3,900 min
3. 7 wk 2 dy
4. 1,488 hr
5. 3 dy 5 hr
6. 1 min 16 sec

7. 1,584 hr
8. 0 min 32 sec
9. 4,440 min
10. 3 dy 19 hr
11. 12 wk 3 dy
12. 4,860 sec

13. 10 wk 3 dy
14. 0 dy 12 hr
15. 1,824 hr
16. 1,200 sec
17. 0 min 36 sec
18. 1,620 min

19. 3,480 min
20. 1,080 min

Page 58:   Time Machine

1. 1) 2:35pm
   2) 14:51
   3) 08:11
   4) 1:40pm
   5) 9pm
   6) 12pm
   7) 23:55
   8) 04:10

Page 59:   Passage of Time 1

1.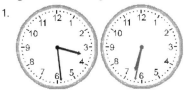
   What time will it be in 3 hours 3 minutes?

2.
   What time will it be in 2 hours 46 minutes?

3.
   What time will it be in 2 hours?

4.
   What time will it be in 3 hours 30 minutes?

5.
   What time will it be in 4 hours 55 minutes?

6.
   What time will it be in 1 hour 3 minutes?

7.
   What time will it be in 5 hours 35 minutes?

8.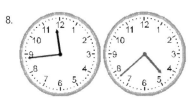
   What time will it be in 4 hours 54 minutes?

Page 60:   Passage of Time 2

1.
   What time was it 2 hours 53 minutes ago?

2.
   What time was it 5 hours 41 minutes ago?

3.
   What time was it 1 hour 1 minute ago?

4.
   What time was it 1 hour 4 minutes ago?

5.
   What time was it 3 hours 28 minutes ago?

6.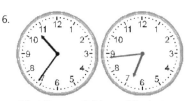
   What time was it 3 hours 52 minutes ago?

7.

What time was it 1 hour 15 minutes ago?

8.

What time was it 2 hours 59 minutes ago?

Page 61: Measuring

1. W=5 H=4 P=18 A=20   2. W=3 H=3 P=12 A=9   3. W=4 H=3 P=14 A=12   4. W=6 H=3 P=18 A=18

5. W=4 H=5 P=18 A=20   6. W=5 H=5 P=20 A=25

Page 62: Measuring Blocks

1. P=30 A=45   2. P=36 A=45   3. P=36 A=63   4. P=30 A=36   5. P=36 A=63   6. P=30 A=36

Page 63: Identify the Temperature

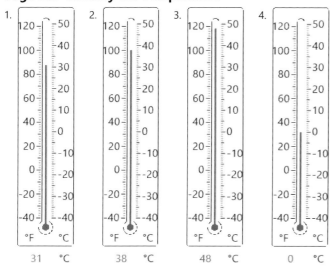

1. 31 °C   2. 38 °C   3. 48 °C   4. 0 °C

Page 63: Shade the Temperature

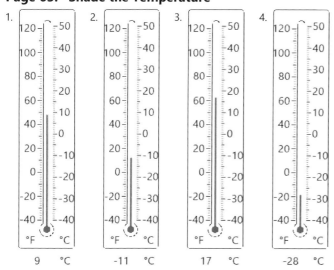

1. 9 °C   2. -11 °C   3. 17 °C   4. -28 °C

Page 64: Measurement Word Questions

1. 169ml

2. 0.11m

3. a) 26cm
   b) 40cm²
   c) (52 x 26) + (52 x 40) = 3432

4. 14g

Page 65: Shopping Problems

1. £2.50   2. £1.40   3. £7.30   4. £3.80   5. £6.30   6. £6.10   7. £2.90   8. £4.90   9. £2.50   10. £2.70

Page 66: Add the Coins

1. £4.07   2. £0.61   3. £1.29   4. £1.27   5. £2.01   6. £4.52   7. £0.56   8. £1.07   9. £0.70   10. £3.20

11. £2.36   12. £2.06

Page 67: Polygons 1

1. Scalene Triangle   2. Regular Hexagon   3. Trapezoid   4. Rhombus   5. Regular Heptagon

6. Parallelogram   7. Rectangle   8. Right Triangle

Page 67: Polygons 2

1. Irregular Quadrilateral   2. Irregular Pentagon   3. Irregular Nonagon   4. Irregular Hexagon

5. Irregular Decagon   6. Irregular Heptagon   7. Irregular Octagon   8. Irregular Pentagon

Page 68: 3-D Polygons

1. 1) Name: Cuboid; Faces: 6
   2) Name: Triangular Prism; Faces: 5
   3) Name: Cube; Faces: 6
   4) Name: Square Based Pyramid; Faces: 5
   5) Name: Cylinder; Faces: 3
   6) Name: Cone; Faces: 2

Page 69: Hexagon and Octagon

1. The hexagon must contain 6 unequal sides; the octagon 8 unequal sides.

Page 69: Defining Shapes

1. a) Nonagon
   b) Triangle
   c) Hexagon

Page 70: Lines of Symmetry

1. Square and Octagon. They are both symmetrical horizontally and vertically.

Page 71: Right Angle

1. Angle 2 is the right angle. It's 90°

Page 71: Obtuse, acute or reflex?

1. 159º Obtuse 2. 258º Reflex 3. 106º Obtuse - *An acute angle is less than 90˚. An obtuse angle is between 90˚ and 180˚. A reflex angle is between 180˚ and 360˚*

Page 72: Angles

1. 127º Obtuse   2. 36º Acute   3. 108º Obtuse   4. 169º Obtuse   5. 142º Obtuse   6. 250º Reflex

From smallest to largest: 1st) 2. 2nd) 3. 3rd) 1. 4th) 5. 5th) 4 6th) 6.

Page 72: Drawing Angles

1. The right angle must be 90° and the acute angle between 0° and 90°

Page 73: Treasure Chest

1. X=4, Y=9 - (4,9)

Page 74: Treasure Chest

1. The quickest way from (6,4) to (4,9) is either i) 2 left and 5 up or ii) 5 up and 2 left

2. From (4,9) to (2,1). The crew must turn 180° and then move i) 2 right and 8 up or ii) 8 up and 2 right. (Rather than down/ left as the crew are facing downwards/ the opposite direction).

Page 75: Bar Chart

1.
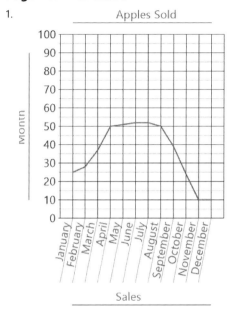

Apples Sold

Sales	Month
January	25
February	28
March	37
April	50
May	51
June	52
July	52
August	50
September	39
October	24
November	10
December	10

Page 76: Bar Chart

1. June and July

2. October

3. 44

4. 3 months

5. 191 apples were sold January - May. The shop owner sold 382 oranges in this time period.

6. 102 sales in July and August. They made £51

Page 77: Pictogram

1. 15 animals   2. 14/15   3. 1/3   4. 27   5. 225 animals   6. 8 tusks

Page 79: Line Graph

1. Tuesday   2. 1110

3. 260   4. 1159

5. 4: Tuesday, Friday, Saturday and Sunday   6. 588

7. Friday

Printed in Great Britain
by Amazon

30015466R00055